THE
CONSUMERS
UNION
REPORT ON
SMOKING
AND THE
PUBLIC
INTEREST

THE CONSUMERS UNION REPORT ON
SMOKING
AND THE PUBLIC INTEREST

By Ruth and Edward Brecher
Arthur Herzog, Walter Goodman, Gerald Walker
and the Editors of Consumer Reports

1963

CONSUMERS UNION, MOUNT VERNON, N.Y.

PUBLISHED BY CONSUMERS UNION OF U.S., INC.
IN ASSOCIATION WITH TEAM JOURNALISM REPORTS
DISTRIBUTED BY SIMON AND SCHUSTER, INC.
ROCKEFELLER CENTER, NEW YORK 20, N.Y.
FIRST PRINTING
DESIGNED BY WILLIAM GROVE
MANUFACTURED IN THE UNITED STATES OF AMERICA
TYPOGRAPHY BY LETTICK TYPOGRAFIC, INC.
◆◆◆◆   PRINTED BY MERCURY LITHOGRAPHING CORP.
LIBRARY OF CONGRESS CATALOG CARD NUMBER: 63-19380

The charts in Part I were prepared by Dyno Lowenstein; the
photographs were taken by Jay Walker of the Veterans Administration Hospital, East Orange, N.J. The cartoon in Part II is by
Robert Day. The cigarette advertisements in Part III are from the
collection of Dr. Michael Shimkin of the U.S. Public Health Service. The anti-smoking posters reproduced in Part IV have been
used in Denmark, Great Britain, and the U.S.S.R.

INTRODUCTION

A teenager just beginning to smoke said, "Nobody young worries much about some disease they might get 40 or 50 years from now." A few million men and women of 40 or 50 or 60 said, "I'd like to stop but I can't." The former president of one of the largest tobacco companies said, "We are not in the cancer research business." And the tobacco companies, in more than $200 million worth of advertising space and time and in a great variety of ways, said, "Smoke!"

In the area bounded by these four points of view the sales of cigarettes in the United States last year reached the total of one half trillion; this was roughly one hundred billion more than were sold in 1953, the year in which the medical evidence linking cigarette smoking to lung cancer first received widespread attention.

As a statistic for the Age of Anxiety, as an item for the Theater of the Absurd, and as a tribute to salesmanship, this figure can only command our respect. On any other ground it must be viewed with real alarm (if we can get past disbelief). And the more than $200 million spent last year for advertising, more than was spent on all but two or three other single products, is hardly less alarming. In ten years of accumulating evidence indicting cigarette smoking as a major health hazard, the annual advertising expenditure has increased 134%. And the number of deaths from lung cancer — a rare disease when cigarette smoking first became popular — last year reached 40,000, about the same as the number of deaths from automobile accidents.

The picture seems out of focus, and the situation almost out of control. Nor do things get clearer as we look harder. The Surgeon General of the U.S. Public Health Service, on three occasions extending over six years, has cited cigarette smoking as one of the major causes of lung cancer, while Congress has turned back every attempt to legislate some kind of control over the risks. The Surgeon General now has an Advisory Committee which is making a new study of the medical problem. The volume of cigarette advertising aimed at teenagers is such that a college newspaper which decided, on the medical evidence, to accept no more such advertising had to appeal for funds in order to continue publication.

The present book is an effort to bring this murky picture into some kind of focus, so that understanding may replace bafflement and out of understanding may come some informed action to deal with what is already a major health problem and is fast becoming a social one.

Consumers Union has tested cigarettes for many years. There seemed some general usefulness in reporting comparative evaluations, if only to provide smokers with an unbiased guide through the thickets of advertising claims to the brands that would probably do them the least harm. And yet, concerning the test statistic that this brand had (at least at the time of test) 13 or 17 milligrams of tar in its smoke as against 22 or 35 for that brand, one could say only that the information might be important. But the medical and social statistic that 1,000,000 *children now of school age may die prematurely of lung cancer is important.*

It seemed necessary, in short, to move beyond testing to deal with cigarettes in the medical and social terms which have come to overshadow all else on this front. And in just such terms the five experienced researchers and writers listed on the title page, who had been brought together by Team Journalism Reports, had already developed plans for a book. On commission from CU they went to work on it. The research tapped the resources of various governmental and private agencies, in which many informed people willingly contributed much time and thought and substance to the book. CU's Medical Adviser served as an active consultant, along with a number of other medical authorities. Member organizations of the International Office of Consumers Unions submitted information on what was going on in their countries. Staff members of CONSUMER REPORTS *worked with the contributors and reviewed and edited the whole work.*

Responsibility for initial drafting of the separate Parts of the book was assigned as follows: Part I — Ruth and Edward Brecher; Part II — Arthur Herzog; Part III — Walter Goodman; Part IV — Gerald Walker. But, as noted above and at the beginning of Part IV, the book was a group undertaking throughout; everyone involved helped everyone else to try to deal broadly, objectively, and as authoritatively as possible with the various aspects of the subject. The subject is, indeed, too important and has come to affect the public interest too deeply to be dealt with in any other way.

Dexter Masters

DIRECTOR
CONSUMERS UNION

CONTENTS

See page 219 for Index

PART I
THE MEDICAL EVIDENCE

PART II
THE INDUSTRY:
SCIENCE & PUBLIC RELATIONS

PART III

THE INDUSTRY: ADVERTISING & HEALTH

PART IV

POINTS FOR A PROGRAM

"For thy sake, tobacco, I would do anything but die."
CHARLES LAMB (circa 1818)

"Do You Inhale?" "What's there to be afraid of?"
FROM A CIGARETTE ADVERTISEMENT (1932)

"If present trends continue lung cancer will claim the lives of more than 1,000,000 present school children in this country before they reach the age of 70 years."
THE AMERICAN PUBLIC HEALTH ASSOCIATION (1959)

PART I
The Medical Evidence

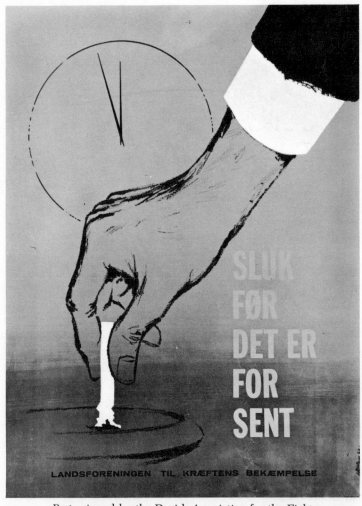

Poster issued by the Danish Association for the Fight
Against Cancer and adapted for the cover of this book
TRANSLATION: *"Put it out before it's too late."*

CHAPTER 1
We Are Living in an Epidemic

IN OCTOBER 1920, a young University of Minnesota pathologist, Dr. Moses Barron, performed an autopsy on a 46-year-old male patient known in the medical records as L.H., and determined that he had died of lung cancer (primary carcinoma of the lung). This seemed curious, for another University of Minnesota pathologist had performed an autopsy two months before on a 42-year-old male patient, and had also found lung cancer. A third death from lung cancer was found later in October.

Dr. Barron had always supposed that cancer of the lung was an exceedingly rare disease. Sometimes several years went by without a single case among University of Minnesota autopsies. Three cases in three months aroused Dr. Barron's interest. During the months that followed, his interest grew, for additional cases turned up at a rapid rate. Startled, now, Dr. Barron went back over the university's autopsy records and unearthed some facts which he reported to the Minnesota State Medical Society meetings on August 25, 1921.

During the 20-year period from 1899 through 1918, Dr. Barron's study revealed, only four cases of lung cancer had been identified at autopsy by University of Minnesota pathologists. There had been only one case in 1919. Yet during the single year from July 1, 1920 through June 30, 1921, eight lung cancer cases had turned up. Was this, perhaps, the onset of an epidemic?

Pathologists generally present their statistics in a standard form: number of autopsies, number of cases of one kind, percentage of these cases to all autopsies. A rate of 0.1 per cent means one case in a thousand autopsies, while 1.0 per cent means one in a hundred. Cast in this form, Dr. Barron's figures revealed the following remarkable increase in lung cancer deaths:

1899 through 1918	0.1%	(4 deaths in 3,399 autopsies)
1919 to July 1921	0.9%	(9 deaths in 1,003 autopsies)

The conclusion seemed inescapable, and Dr. Barron cautiously drew it in 1921. "This disease," he wrote, "is apparently increasing in frequency, especially during the past few years." And he was right. For the period 1949 through 1952 the University of Minnesota rate reached 3.2 per cent (264 lung cancer deaths in 8,332 autopsies).

In various other parts of the world, autopsy records were telling substantially the same story. A rise was quite generally apparent, earlier in some places, later in others, often at about the same time as Dr. Barron's findings. Here, for example, are lung cancer rates drawn at five-year intervals from the autopsy records of the Charité Hospital in Berlin:

1908	0.3%	1918	0.6%
1913	0.4%	1923	1.5%

And here are the figures, for five-year periods, from Zurich, Switzerland:

1906-1910	0.1%	1916-1920	0.7%
1911-1915	0.5%	1921-1925	2.1%

All of the autopsy records, it is true, did not fit precisely this pattern. At the Royal Infirmary in Manchester, England, for example, the increase which Dr. Barron had noted in 1921 was visible much earlier. In Reykjavik, Iceland, lung cancer rates at autopsy remained low as late as 1948. But by and large the trend has been irregularly upward ever since about 1920.

An autopsy series of particular value comes from Presbyterian Hospital in New York City, where Dr. David M. Spain reviewed the autopsy findings for the 45-year period from 1912 through 1956. The diagnosis of lung cancer depends primarily on the microscopic examination of cells taken from the lungs; Presbyterian Hospital had maintained microphotographs of cancer cells for its earlier autopsies and had actually preserved the cells themselves in microscope slides for the later autopsies, so that Dr. Spain was able to review the entire series personally and confirm or correct the diagnoses. His figures showed the following increase in lung cancer deaths:

1912-1921	0.6%	(6 deaths in 992 autopsies)
1922-1931	1.3%	(21 deaths in 1,649 autopsies)
1932-1941	2.8%	(83 deaths in 2,950 autopsies)
1942-1946	3.4%	(49 deaths in 1,449 autopsies)
1947-1956	3.7%	(120 deaths in 3,250 autopsies)

What was happening at Presbyterian Hospital was also happening at the University of Michigan, where 14,000 autopsies were performed from 1895 through 1954. As at Presbyterian Hospital, materials from the earlier University of Michigan autopsies were preserved and reviewed from time to time to confirm the lung cancer diagnoses and to make sure that cases diagnosable as lung cancer by modern standards had not been missed during the earlier years. The figures show a remarkably steady rise in lung cancer incidence for each thousand autopsies in the series:

CASES OF LUNG CANCER

1st thousand	0.2%	8th thousand	2.2%
2nd thousand	0.8	9th thousand	2.4
3rd thousand	1.0	10th thousand	2.6
4th thousand	1.4	11th thousand	3.1
5th thousand	1.8	12th thousand	3.9
6th thousand	2.1	13th thousand	3.4
7th thousand	2.2	14th thousand	4.2

The rate thus rose from 0.2 per cent to 4.2 per cent during the sixty-year period from 1895 through 1954 — more than a twenty-fold increase. (Comparable figures for University of Michigan autopsies since 1954 are not available.)

THE DEATH RATE EVIDENCE. The autopsy figures presented above are all subject to a major shortcoming. They include for the most part only patients who died in hospitals and whose relatives consented to an autopsy. Evidence concerning so highly selected a group cannot be uncritically applied to the population as a whole. Suppose, for example, that during the early years of a series most lung cancer patients died at home; and that as time passed a larger and larger proportion died in hospitals and came to autopsy. This trend of events might have produced an *apparent* increase in lung cancer of the kind described above without any *actual* increase in the disease. To rule out this and other possibilities of this kind, the causes of deaths in a total population rather than an autopsied population must be considered. For this purpose death certificates

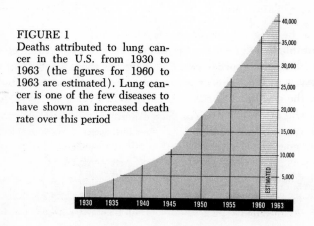

FIGURE 1
Deaths attributed to lung cancer in the U.S. from 1930 to 1963 (the figures for 1960 to 1963 are estimated). Lung cancer is one of the few diseases to have shown an increased death rate over this period

offer the broadest possible evidence. And the death certificate data fully confirm the data from autopsies.

In the United States, for example, only 371 deaths were attributed to lung cancer in 1914. This number rose to 2,357 in 1930, 7,121 in 1940, 18,313 in 1950, and 36,420 in 1960. FIGURE 1 shows the increase year by year from 1930 on.

This increase in number of deaths suggests the reason for the increasing public health concern with lung cancer. But the raw figures require corrections of several types. The U.S. population, for example, increased rapidly between 1914 and 1960; and the proportion of the population covered by uniform death certificate reporting also increased. Further, lung cancer is a disease of middle age and old age, and the proportion of the population living into the lung cancer age brackets increased considerably. Finally, the figures for the total population mask the marked differences between what was happening to lung cancer in men and in women. FIGURE 2, accordingly, makes allowances for these factors.

This epidemic, moreover, has not been limited to the United States. Indeed, the rise among men in Scotland, England, Wales, Finland, and some other countries has been even steeper.

COMBINING THE EVIDENCE. Just as the autopsy evidence may be doubted on the ground that the sample of deaths coming to autopsy is a selected and untypical sample, so it is possible to doubt the death certificate evidence on the ground that physicians who fill out the certificates are not always sure of what really caused the death — and, in some cases, they may be merely guessing. Neither kind of evidence by itself proves that there was an actual increase in lung cancer deaths.

But when the autopsy evidence is combined with the death certificate evidence, the proof emerges very clearly. The figures based on autopsies performed by skilled pathologists at the world's great medical centers cannot be dismissed as mere guesswork; and the lung cancer death rates covering substantially all of the deaths in a dozen different countries cannot be dismissed as due to biased sampling. The criticisms of each body of evidence are answered by the fact that the other body of evidence tells the same story.

This theme of combining the evidence will reappear throughout this discussion. Only rarely can a single study, observation, or experiment stand by itself. Each of the studies we will re-

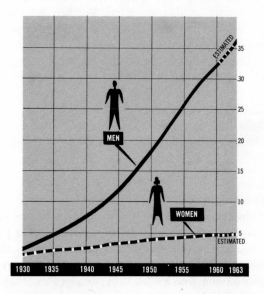

FIGURE 2
Deaths attributed to lung cancer per 100,000 men and women in the U.S. from 1930 to 1963 (the figures for 1960 to 1963 are estimated). The figures are weighted to allow for the gradual aging of the population

18

port is subject to qualifications and limitations. But the points not covered in one study are soon covered by another study. Thus a wall of evidence is gradually erected.

IMPROVED DIAGNOSIS. During the early years of the lung cancer epidemic it was sometimes argued that the apparent increase in the disease might result from improved methods of diagnosis among physicians filling out death certificates, and from a greater alertness to lung cancer among pathologists performing autopsies.

No doubt a part of the apparent increase is due to such factors. But many separate lines of evidence indicate that most of the apparent increase is in fact a true increase.

First, the simple bulk of the increase makes improved diagnosis an inadequate explanation. Physicians and university pathologists prior to the 1920s might conceivably have missed one-half of the lung cancer deaths, though that is most unlikely. But it is utterly inconceivable that they should have missed nine lung cancer deaths out of every ten or nineteen out of every twenty.

Second, improvements in diagnosis also occurred with respect to such forms of cancer as stomach cancer. Yet no comparable rise in reported cancer rates generally, or in cancer at other internal sites, has occurred.

Third, lung cancer is as easy to diagnose among women as among men. The proportion of the increase due to improved diagnosis must therefore make its appearance in the women's rate as well as the men's rate. Even if the entire increase in lung cancer among women shown in FIGURE 2 were attributed to improved diagnosis – a most dubious assumption – the far more rapid increase among men would remain unexplained.

Fourth, the attempt to explain away the increase as merely the result of improved diagnosis comes to grief on the rock of the well established fact that, to this very day, cancer of the

19

lung remains a rare disease among certain groups of people.

Among Seventh Day Adventists, for example, the disease is almost unknown, and the few cases which do occur are primarily in recent converts. Lung cancer is as easy to diagnose in Seventh Day Adventists as in Baptists, Methodists, Catholics, Jews or atheists. If the lung cancer increase were merely the result of improved diagnosis, the Seventh Day Adventist rate would be expected to rise with the other rates. (We shall have more to say about this fortunate group later on.)

Finally, there is the strange but unchallenged fact that lung cancer remains today a rare disease among men and women who do not smoke and who never have smoked. It is also relatively uncommon among men who smoke cigars or pipes or both, but not cigarettes. Improved diagnosis, to the extent that it has affected the statistics through the years, would have produced a rise among non-smokers, pipe smokers, and cigar smokers as well as among cigarette smokers. The excess rise among cigarette smokers cannot be explained by improved diagnosis.

The conclusion is inescapable, and even spokesmen for the cigarette industry today rarely seek to escape it: We are living in the midst of a major lung cancer epidemic. This epidemic hit men first and hardest, but has affected women as well. It is occurring not only in the United States but in a number of other countries. It cannot be explained away by such factors as improved diagnosis. And, as FIGURE 3 indicates, there is reason to believe that the worst is yet to come.

The American Public Health Association has called attention to this black future in a single dramatic statistic. If present trends continue, the Association reported in 1959, "lung cancer will claim the lives of more than 1,000,000 present school children in this country before they reach the age of 70 years."

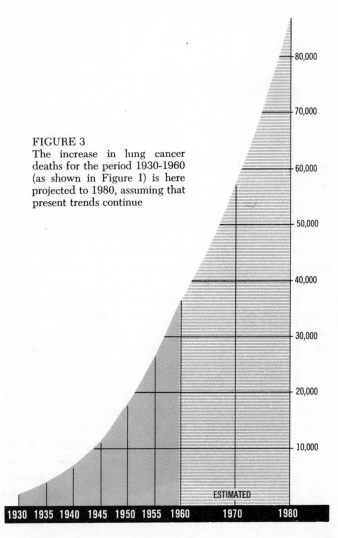

FIGURE 3
The increase in lung cancer deaths for the period 1930-1960 (as shown in Figure I) is here projected to 1980, assuming that present trends continue

CHAPTER 2
The Statistical Evidence

MORE THAN 400 years ago, in 1556 A.D., George Agricola published what may well be the first report on lung cancer, and the first explanation of it. Agricola was the town physician in Joachimsthal in Bohemia (now Jáchymov in Czechoslovakia), and his classic treatise on mining, *De Re Metallica,* called attention to a disease of the lungs shockingly prevalent then and later among workers in the Joachimsthal mines. Here is his description, translated from the Latin by Dr. (later President) and Mrs. Herbert C. Hoover:

> "Some mines are so dry that they are entirely devoid of water, and this dryness causes the workmen . . . harm, for the dust which is stirred and beaten up by digging penetrates into the windpipe and lungs, and produces difficulty in breathing. . . . If the dust has corrosive qualities, it eats away the lungs, and implants consumption in the bodies; hence in the mines of the Carpathian mountains women are found who have married seven husbands, all of whom this terrible consumption has carried off to a premature death."

The mine dust in these and similar mines — so vividly described by Agricola — contained a number of substances which might explain the lung cancer, including radium and uranium. Indeed, it was from Joachimsthal pitchblende that the Curies in 1898 isolated radium. Other suspected agents in the dust were arsenic, nickel, and cobalt. Studies published in the 1930s indicated that, as is often the case with cancer, the agent required many years before death from lung cancer ensued.

From 13 to 23 years elapsed between the time a boy or man went to work in the mines and his death from lung cancer.

Among other occupational groups, too, very high lung cancer rates have been reported. One such group was composed of employees of six American chromate plants during the years 1940-1948. Their lung cancer death rate was 29 times as high as the rate for U.S. males generally.

Among nickel workers in South Wales from 1948 to 1956, the lung cancer rate was five times as high as among workers in other occupations.

And among workers employed in the dusty areas of an English asbestos plant for 15 years or more, the lung cancer rate was 30 times greater than for males in England and Wales generally.

THE CORRELATION STUDIES. Findings such as these among workers exposed to specific dusts or pollutants provide valuable clues to the more general lung cancer mystery. They indicate that lung cancer can follow inhalation of damaging substances, and that many years of exposure may precede death. In seeking to explain the general increase in lung cancer after 1920, accordingly, the thoughts of researchers often turned to the Joachimsthal miners, and some substance was sought which fitted the following description and which might therefore explain the lung cancer epidemic:

1. It must enter the human lung.
2. It must have come into common use in countries like England and the U.S. about 1900.
3. It must be in very common use in countries where lung cancer rates are high but less common in countries where lung cancer rates are low.
4. It must enter men's lungs more than women's lungs.

An obvious candidate for this role is cigarette smoke, and many studies have confirmed the extent to which it meets the description of a substance entering the lungs which has increased along with lung cancer — allowing a lag of 15 to 30 years between the smoking rate and the lung cancer rate.

Most striking are recent figures from Iceland, where lung cancer remained a rare disease and cigarette smoking a relatively unpopular habit as recently as 1940. Since then, cigarette smoking has become increasingly popular — and lung cancer increasingly common. Here are the figures from the University of Iceland Department of Pathology, showing the proportion of autopsies in which death from lung cancer was found:

1932-1940	0.5%	(3 deaths in	644	autopsies)
1941-1945	0.6%	(3 deaths in	478	autopsies)
1946-1950	1.3%	(8 deaths in	636	autopsies)
1951-1955	2.2%	(17 deaths in	781	autopsies)
1956-1960	2.6%	(31 deaths in	1,174	autopsies)

Iceland, in short, took up cigarette smoking later than other countries — and the lung cancer epidemic hit Iceland later than it hit other countries.

The Icelandic increase cannot be attributed to air pollution, Dr. Niels Dungal of the University of Iceland points out, for at least since 1943 Reykjavik (where most of the deaths occurred) has had the purest air in Europe. A municipal heating system based on hot springs near the city has replaced both coal and oil for heating purposes.

Such data — and many additional correlations between cigarette consumption in one year and lung cancer deaths in a later year — do not, of course, "prove" that cigarette smoking is the "cause" of lung cancer. They merely indicate that smoking is a likely suspect. Other substances — for example, air pollution in general, or industrial wastes and products of industrial and domestic combustion discharged into the air through smokestacks and chimneys, or particles released into the air by the wearing of rubber tires on paved surfaces —

24

might also fit the requirements of the role. Yet a little thought will show that the correlations between cigarette smoking and lung cancer deaths do have considerable value as evidence, for no equally impressive body of correlations exists with respect to any other factor.

THE RETROSPECTIVE STUDIES. Fortunately we do not have to rely on mere correlations to decide the issue. Through the years scientists have developed a type of investigation known as the "retrospective study," and at least 27 such studies of lung cancer have been published.

These retrospective studies all consist essentially in starting with a group of lung cancer victims and asking this question:

What has occurred in their past histories which might explain their lung cancers?

One early answer came from an English physician, Dr. F. E. Tylecote. He reported in the British medical journal *Lancet* in 1927 that, in almost every case of lung cancer he had seen or known about, the patient was a regular smoker, usually of cigarettes.

This kind of evidence, of course, leaves much to be desired. How many cases of lung cancer had Dr. Tylecote seen or known about? How many exceptions were there to his statement that "almost every case" was a regular smoker? And what did he mean by the term "regular smoker"?

A somewhat more specific answer came from Drs. Aaron Arkin and David H. Wagner of Chicago. They reported in *The Journal of the American Medical Association* for Februrary 22, 1936, that of 135 men with lung cancer they had examined, 90 per cent were "chronic smokers." This kind of evidence is significant. If someone were to report, for example, that among patients with a particular kind of blood disease 90 per cent were users of a certain drug, the Food and Drug Administration would no doubt be urged to launch an immediate investigation. But findings like those of Arkin and Wagner, while suggestive, still hardly constitute proof; for example, they did not rule out the chance that 90 per cent of the men of the same age, occupations, and residence in Chicago who did *not* die of lung cancer might also be "chronic smokers."

The next step, accordingly, was to launch controlled retrospective studies, in which each patient with lung cancer was matched as closely as possible with a control who did not have lung cancer, in order to determine significant differences between the lung cancer victims and the controls.

One early controlled study was reported by Dr. F. H. Müller from Cologne, Germany, in 1939. Müller compared 80 male lung cancer patients with 80 healthy men and found much more smoking among the cancer patients. He concluded that smoking must be responsible to a marked degree for lung cancer.

Such a study, of course, is subject to the objection that it all depends on how you select your controls. Later studies, accordingly, have used great care in matching each lung cancer patient with a similar control case — usually a hospital patient with some other disease — of the same age, sex, residential area, occupational class, and so on.

An excellent example of such a critically controlled study was reported from England in 1950 by Drs. W. Richard Doll and A. Bradford Hill. They began with 1,465 lung cancer patients, mostly from London hospitals. Each of these patients was matched by age and sex with a hospital patient who did not have lung cancer. Some of the control patients had cancer at other sites; some had diseases other than cancer. Like the earlier studies, this Doll and Hill study reported a significant association between smoking, especially cigarette smoking, and lung cancer. Here are two of the findings from this controlled survey:

Only one male lung cancer patient in 200 was a non-smoker, as compared with one in 22 among the controls.

One male lung cancer smoker in four was a "heavy smoker" (carefully defined as a man smoking more than 25 cigarettes a day or the equivalent in pipe tobacco), as compared with only one in eight among the controls.

Critics of these retrospective studies might suspect that the interviewers who ask patients about their smoking habits could bias the results by consciously or unconsciously "leading" lung cancer patients to exaggerate their smoking, and not leading the control patients to the same extent. Doll and Hill were able to exclude this possibility. In some cases, the patients were interviewed at a time when it was supposed that they had lung cancer, but the diagnosis later proved to be erroneous. If the interviewers were leading the lung cancer patients to exaggerate their smoking habits, there would have been an excess proportion of heavy smokers in this group. No such excess was found.

The Doll-Hill study might also be criticized on the ground that the control group was itself composed of hospitalized patients and might therefore not be typical of the population as a whole. So, as an added precaution, Doll and Hill made a further study of a random sample of the English population as a whole. Far from exaggerating the relationship between lung cancer and smoking, this additional study revealed, the use of hospital patients as controls actually minimized the relationship, for there were more smokers and heavy smokers in the control group than in the population as a whole.

A study of the same kind, made in the United States by Drs. Ernest L. Wynder and Evarts A. Graham, then at the Washington University School of Medicine in St. Louis, was also published in 1950. They also took numerous precautions to avoid bias. In one part of their study, for example, their interviewers talked with all the patients coming to a chest clinic, without knowing whether the patients had lung cancer or some other chest condition. The diagnosis was not recorded until after smoking habits had been ascertained. Using these and other precautions, Drs. Wynder and Graham were able to draw such impressive conclusions as these:

"Excessive and prolonged use of tobacco, especially cigarettes, seems to be an important factor in the induction of bronchogenic carcinoma." [For definitions, see page 38.]

"Among 605 men with bronchogenic carcinoma . . . 96.5% were moderately heavy to chain smokers for many years, compared with 73.7% among the general male population without cancer. Among the cancer group 51.2% were excessive or chain smokers compared with 19.1% in the general hospital group without cancer."

"The occurrence of carcinoma of the lung in a male non-smoker or minimal smoker is a rare phenomenon."

"96.1% of patients with cancer of the lungs who had a history of smoking had smoked for over twenty years. Few women have smoked for such a length of time [as of 1950], and this is believed to be one of the reasons for the greater incidence of the disease among men today."

"94.1% of male patients with cancer of the lungs were found to be cigarette smokers, 4.0% pipe smokers, and 3.5% cigar smokers. This prevalence of cigarette smoking is greater than among the general hospital population of the same age group. The greater practice of inhalation among cigarette smokers is believed to be a factor in the increased incidence of the disease."

THE SEVENTH DAY ADVENTIST STUDY. These and other retrospective studies of this kind, which start with lung cancer victims and work backward, are subject to a common flaw. They do not foreclose the possibility that *some other factor associated with smoking* — call it the X-factor — may be the "cause" of the lung cancer.

An example will illustrate this possibility. Heavy cigarette smokers are more likely than non-smokers to develop cirrhosis of the liver. But this does not mean that heavy cigarette smoking "causes" cirrhosis of the liver. Rather, the relationship seems to involve these links:

1. Most heavy drinkers are also heavy smokers.
2. Many heavy drinkers suffer from dietary deficiencies.
3. These dietary deficiencies, in all probability, lead in turn to cirrhosis of the liver.

Heavy drinking, in short, is in all probability the X-factor by which heavy cigarette smoking is linked with dietary deficiencies and thus with cirrhosis of the liver.

It is hard to conceive of such a specific X-factor linking smoking with lung cancer, however — and the inherent implausibility of such a factor has been dramatically illustrated in a remarkable study made by Drs. Wynder, Frank R. Lemon, and Irwin J. Bross at Seventh Day Adventist hospitals throughout the country.

These Seventh Day Adventist hospitals are good hospitals, staffed with competent pathologists and diagnosticians. They treat both Seventh Day Adventists and patients of other creeds, or of no creed whatever. The study sought essentially an answer to this question:

Is there a lung cancer difference between Seventh Day Adventists and others treated in the same hospitals?

The answer, as in other retrospective studies reviewed above, was clear-cut. Patients at these hospitals who were not Seventh Day Adventists had just about the lung cancer rates to be expected. Among Seventh Day Adventists, in contrast, lung cancer was almost totally unknown. Only two cases were diagnosed among many hundreds of patients dying of other diseases. And both of these cases, interestingly enough, were among recent converts to Seventh Day Adventism.

Now let us consider the light this finding throws on the X-factor. If such a factor exists, it must (of course) have the two characteristics already noted: it must be associated with cigarette smoking (as distinct from cigar or pipe smoking); and it must cause lung cancer. In addition, we can affirm on the basis of the Seventh Day Adventist findings, the X-factor must be present in Catholics, Methodists, Baptists, Jews, and atheists — but Seventh Day Adventists (except recent converts) must somehow be resistant to or lacking in it altogether!

There is, of course, a much simpler and more plausible explanation of the findings. *Seventh Day Adventists seldom smoke.*

This simpler theory is buttressed by the fact that both of the converts to Seventh Day Adventism who developed lung cancer smoked a pack a day or more for 20 years or longer prior to their conversion.

COMBINING THE EVIDENCE. Once again, no single retrospective study by itself can *prove* a significant association between cigarette smoking and lung cancer. Each study is subject to qualifications. But when the 27 or more retrospective studies are considered in combination, their joint probative value is very high.

The studies were made independently, by different scientists or groups. At least one study was launched with the expectation of *disproving* an association. Parallel results have been reported from the U.S., England, Germany, Japan, The Netherlands, Denmark, and other countries. The association was shown to hold for women as well as men, and for various age groups considered separately.

Finally, it should be noted that the retrospective data reviewed in this section and the correlation data in the section immediately preceding are independent findings which reinforce one another. The two kinds of data taken jointly have a probative value in excess of either taken alone.

THE NEGATIVE EVIDENCE. Let us next consider controlled retrospective studies which show the absence of an association between cigarette smoking and lung cancer. This can be briefly done.

There are no such studies.

No one has ever matched lung cancer victims with comparable controls and reported that the lung cancer victims smoked less than the controls, or smoked only to the same extent, or smoked only a little bit more.

If a single population could be found — urban or rural, domestic or foreign, red, yellow, black, or white — in which an increase in lung cancer is *not* linked with heavy, prolonged cigarette smoking, the case against the cigarette would concededly be weakened. But no such population has been reported.

Some widely publicized reports, it is true, may seem at first glance to provide negative evidence casting doubt on the cigarette-lung cancer theory. Let us consider three of these reports.

Dr. Geoffrey Dean noted in 1959 that white males born in South Africa were among the world's heaviest smokers, yet they had a lower lung cancer rate than male immigrants to South Africa from Britain. This seemed to suggest that something in the British environment, perhaps air pollution, was more important than smoking.

Dr. D. F. Eastcott reported similarly from New Zealand in 1956 that immigrants from Britain to New Zealand smoked no more than native white New Zealanders but had a higher lung cancer rate.

Finally, Dr. Jacob Cohen of New York University (an American Tobacco Company consultant) and Robert K. Heimann of the American Tobacco Company alleged in 1962 that employees of the cigarette division of the American Tobacco Company smoked very heavily, yet had no deaths from primary lung cancer and were very healthy in other respects. Dr. Cohen and Mr. Heimann described both their own figures and the South African and New Zealand figures as "negative findings" with respect to the cigarette-lung cancer hypothesis.

But none of these studies provided a matched comparison between smokers and non-smokers alike in other respects. Instead, all three studies lumped smokers and non-smokers together, and thus actually concealed the smoking effect.

The danger of relying on such uncontrolled studies can be dramatically illustrated. At about the same time that Dr. Cohen and Mr. Heimann published their American Tobacco Company study with its review of the South African and New Zealand studies, Dr. Dean published additional figures from South Africa in the *British Medical Journal*. The additional report contained detailed comparisons of smokers and non-smokers missing from the earlier study. With this missing data supplied, the picture turned out to be very different.

Cigarette smokers, the new study revealed, had a much higher lung cancer death rate than non-smokers. Further, this variation of lung cancer rates with smoking habits appeared both among men born in South Africa and among the immigrants from Britain. Again, the amount of lung cancer turned out to vary directly with the amount of smoking; native-born South African males who did not smoke, for example, had a lung cancer death rate of eight per 100,000 as compared with a rate of 156 among native-born South African males who smoked 50 or more cigarettes daily. And finally, the significance of the smoking factor turned out to dwarf the significance of the immigration factor which had loomed so large when it was presented in the earlier paper without the smoking-non-smoking comparison. Far from casting doubt on the cigarette-lung cancer hypothesis, the complete South African figures with the smoking-non-smoking comparison included turned out to be one of the most impressive sets of statistics ever compiled in support of the cigarette-lung cancer theory.

Figures for New Zealand and for employees of the American Tobacco Company showing smokers and non-smokers separately have not to date been published.

THE PROSPECTIVE STUDIES. Like any other single kind of evidence, the retrospective studies we have been reviewing are not by themselves conclusive. But they do not stand alone. Even more impressive evidence of the cigarette-lung cancer relationship has been accumulated since 1954 in a series of prospective studies.

Such studies essentially start with groups of presumably healthy smokers and a second group of presumably healthy non-smokers, and follow them through a subsequent period of months or years to find out what happens to both groups.

One important prospective study was conducted in England for the Medical Research Council by Drs. Doll and Hill, whose retrospective study has already been discussed. They began by sending a questionnaire on personal smoking habits to 60,000 British physicians aged 35 or over. Sufficient data to classify the physicians by their smoking habits were received from 40,000. After following the 40,000 physicians for the next 4½ years, Drs. Doll and Hill were able to draw the following conclusions:

Mild smokers are seven times as likely to die of lung cancer as non-smokers.

Moderate smokers are 12 times as likely to die of lung cancer as non-smokers.

Immoderate smokers are 24 times as likely to die of lung cancer as non-smokers.

Because this study was limited to a well-defined population — British physicians over 35 in 1951 — it had certain advantages. For example, the death certificates of *all* physicians who died could be checked, to make sure that those participating in the study were typical of the whole group. The study was on a relatively small scale, however, and it might be argued that physicians are not necessarily typical of the general population. The American prospective study by Drs. E. Cuyler Hammond and Daniel Horn for the American Cancer Society is subject to neither of these two possible qualifications.

These investigators started by training a group of 22,000 cancer society volunteers to get smoking questionnaires from their friends. The volunteers secured usable questionnaires from nearly 190,000 white males aged 50 to 69 who seemed well when questioned. During the next 44 months 187,783 of these men were followed, and 11,870 deaths among them were reported.

The results were so voluminous that only a few can be presented here. The lung cancer death rate per 100,000 men per year for non-smokers was 12.8, indicating that lung cancer is still a rare disease among non-smokers. Among those who smoked from one-half to one pack a day the comparable rate was 107.8. Among those who smoked from one to two packs a day the rate was 229.2. And among those who smoked more than two packs a day it was 264.2. For further details, see pages 36-37.

The prospective study by the late Dr. Harold F. Dorn was very closely in line with the studies of Drs. Doll and Hill and of Drs. Hammond and Horn. He followed nearly 200,000 veterans holding government life insurance policies for a period of 2½ years, and reported that in this group cigarette smokers generally were nearly ten times as likely to die of lung cancer as non-smokers — and that men smoking more than a pack a day were some 16 times as likely to die of lung cancer as non-smokers.

Dr. Lester Breslow of the California State Health Department and his associates have published another prospective study which is of particular interest because it was not designed primarily to check on smoking and lung cancer. On the

34

contrary, it was concerned with employees engaged in types of work which (it was suspected) might lead to high lung cancer rates. The Breslow study did find that some occupational groups had higher lung cancer rates than others; but it also showed that some occupational groups smoked more than others, and it was the groups which smoked most that had the highest lung cancer death rates. The effect of smoking on the lung cancer death rate was so intense that it proved impossible to determine whether or not other occupational factors were also at work.

A different, non-prospective kind of study has been pioneered by William Haenszel and his National Cancer Institute associates. They determined "standard lung cancer mortality rates" for men of various ages in various parts of the country, native-born and foreign-born. Among their impressive findings was the fact that regular cigarette smokers were far more likely to die of lung cancer than non-smokers *in every group they checked.* Here are some examples:

	STANDARD LUNG CANCER MORTALITY RATES FOR MEN WHO ARE NOT REGULAR CIGARETTE SMOKERS	STANDARD LUNG CANCER MORTALITY RATES FOR MEN WHO ARE REGULAR CIGARETTE SMOKERS
Foreign-born	61	277
Native-born	26	180
Born and currently living on farm	11	111
Born and currently living in a large city	34	198

Clearly there are differences between native-born and foreign-born populations, and between city and farm residents; but the differences between regular cigarette smokers and others dwarf all other variations.

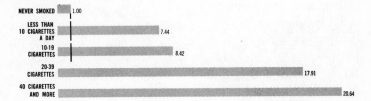

MORTALITY RATIOS for lung cancer deaths by
number of cigarettes smoked daily. This diagram
is based on the findings of one of the most comprehensive studies made to date (the Hammond-Horn
study); but all studies have shown similar results

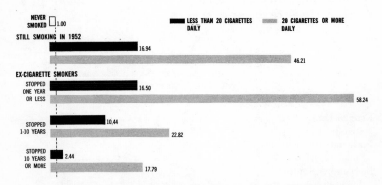

MORTALITY RATIOS for lung cancer deaths in terms of smoking habits (also from the Hammond-Horn study and based on
well-established cases of the two most common kinds of lung
cancer linked to smoking — epidermoid and undifferentiated carcinoma). The relatively high figure for smokers who had stopped
for one year or less is explained by the fact that many of these
smokers stopped because of the onset of disease symptoms

The most recent of the prospective studies, conducted again by Dr. Hammond for the American Cancer Society, is also the largest and broadest. Launched in 1959, it covers more than a million men and women in more than a thousand counties, and it is collecting far more information about each participant than earlier studies did. It is concerned not only with smoking and cancer, but with many other health problems as well. Preliminary findings are in line with the earlier studies, but go beyond them in significant respects. For example, lung cancer turns out to be closely associated with the inhaling of cigarette smoke; indeed, inhaling may prove to be an even more important factor in lung cancer than the number of cigarettes smoked — a point we will discuss at more length further on.

As in the case of controlled retrospective studies, no prospective studies have failed to show a relationship between cigarette smoking and lung cancer.

A few definitions

The term "cancer of the lung" has various meanings in various contexts; a few definitions may prove helpful.

Carcinoma is cancer which arises from skin cells or from the cells lining the mouth, bronchial tubes, stomach, and other "hollow organs." The other main kind of cancer is *sarcoma*. Almost all lung cancer is carcinoma.

Primary carcinoma of the lung means cancer which has originated in the lung rather than spreading or metastasizing to the lung from some other site.

Bronchogenic carcinoma is cancer of the lung originating in the lining cells of the bronchial tubes which distribute air through the lung. This is by far the commonest kind of lung cancer.

Epidermoid carcinoma, undifferentiated carcinoma, and *adenocarcinoma* are the three major kinds of bronchogenic carcinoma. (These can be identified only by microscopic examination of the cancer cells.) Smoking is most closely linked with the first two of these three.

In this presentation, "cancer of the lung" usually means bronchogenic cancer. Where statistics refer to lung cancer generally, or to bronchogenic cancer generally, they usually *understate* the true relationship between smoking and lung cancer. The most impressive statistics are those which link smoking directly to epidermoid and undifferentiated carcinoma of the lung. In one study, for example, these two forms of cancer were found to be *88 times as frequent* among heavy cigarette smokers as among non-smokers. Most studies refer to lung cancer or bronchogenic cancer generally because more precise data are not available.

CHAPTER 3
The Experimental Evidence

EFFORTS have occasionally been made to discredit the kinds of evidence we have been describing on the grounds that they are "merely statistical." This kind of criticism overlooks the fact that some of the central findings of science are supported solely by statistical evidence. The death of a smoker from lung cancer is not a "merely statistical" death; it is a real death. Grouping a dead smoker with large numbers of other smokers who have died of lung cancer does not alter the death or make it "merely statistical"; it simply collects the evidence from many thousands of individual cases into a coherent pattern.

The argument against placing too much reliance on "merely statistical" evidence has perhaps been expressed most forcefully by a scientist who is himself a statistician – Dr. Jacob Yerushalmy of the University of California. He likes to tell the story of a study he made on cigarette smoking during pregnancy. His study revealed, as several others have also revealed, that women who smoke during pregnancy give birth to babies who weigh less on the average than the babies of women who do not smoke. Dr. Yerushalmy's study went further, however; it showed that the weight of the babies was also lower than average among women whose *husbands* smoked, whatever the mothers' own smoking habits!

Since the relationship between a woman's smoking during pregnancy and the weight of her baby is a plausible one in terms of everything known about the physiology of smoking, pregnancy, and birth weight, it is easily accepted. But a change in an infant's birth weight due to the smoking habits of its mother's husband seems unlikely enough to call for some other explanation of the apparent relationship. Let us not rely on a "merely statistical" relationship, Dr. Yerushalmy's story suggests, unless the relationship is a reasonable one.

Such warnings apply with very great force, of course, to findings based on any single statistical study. They may maintain considerable force when applied to groups of statistical studies which pursue a single statistical method — the whole group of retrospective studies described above, for example. But they lose much of their effectiveness when used to attack findings confirmed by divergent statistical techniques, such as the combined correlation data, retrospective data, and prospective data reviewed above.

Still, Dr. Yerushalmy's story does have significance in connection with the smoking-lung cancer relationship. It suggests that the overwhelming statistical evidence we have reviewed would take on an even greater probative force if it could be shown through experimental and pathological studies that a relationship between smoking and lung cancer is inherently plausible as well as statistically evident.

Evidence bearing on the inherent plausibility of the smoking-lung cancer hypothesis will accordingly be reviewed in this chapter. But first it is necessary to recall a few underlying facts about cancer in general.

THE INHERENT NATURE OF CANCER. The human body, like plants and animals generally, is composed of myriads of cells. Each cell divides from time to time, giving rise to two daughter cells. Typically the daughter cells precisely resemble the parent cell.

Each cell has a nucleus, which can be seen through the microscope. In the nuclei are chromosomes, which can also be seen through the microscope and mapped. The chromosomes are composed of DNA (deoxyribonucleic acid). This substance carries a "genetic code." The two daughter cells generally follow the same pattern as their parent cell because they contain the same DNA in the chromosomes of their nuclei and thus receive the same "message" in the genetic code.

Cancer cells, it is generally agreed, arise out of normal cells. But they have been altered in significant respects. They are generally larger and more irregular than ordinary cells; and instead of developing normally they grow wild. The daughter cells into which a cancer cell divides are themselves cancer cells. Instead of dividing and multiplying in accordance with the needs of the organism, they divide and multiply without limit. And instead of respecting the boundaries of nearby tissues as do normal cells, they invade nearby tissues and exhaust their supply of nutrients. Eventually, unless the cancer cells are all removed by surgery or killed by radiation or chemicals, they destroy other tissues and cause death.

Evidence increasingly indicates that it is changes in the DNA chromosomes of a cell which convert it from normal to cancerous. Indeed, chromosome abnormalities in cancer cells can in some instances actually be identified with a microscope. A normal cell does not ordinarily become a cancer cell, or give rise to a cancer daughter cell, at a single moment in time or even overnight. Rather, it appears, the conversion from normal cells to true cancer cells is accomplished through stages.

The first step is *hyperplasia*. This means simply that the cells divide more often, so that the number of cells at a particular place in a particular tissue increases. Instead of one layer or two of lining cells in the breathing passages, for example, five or six layers may be produced, or a dozen. Chronic irritation, mechanical or chemical, may produce this hyperplasia or excessive growth. The calluses on the palms of your hand which you get when you chop wood day after day are a familiar example of hyperplasia due to irritation.

The next step is *metaplasia*. This means an alteration in the cell itself, and perhaps in the DNA chromosomes in its nuclei. Since these altered or metaplastic cells give rise to daughter cells which resemble themselves, a *lesion* often develops — that is, a group of neighboring metaplastic cells.

At first these groups of metaplastic cells continue to live within their own proper boundaries. Some pathologists, accordingly, do not consider such lesions cancerous. Others call them cancer *in situ* —that is, cancer which keeps its place and does not invade neighboring tissues.

The final step occurs when the cells destroy the boundaries of their native tissue and invade neighboring tissues. Also, cells from the original lesion break loose and migrate to other parts of the body where their daughter cells build additional tumors, a process called *metastasis*. A cancer is generally curable if it is surgically removed or if all the cells are killed before metastasis occurs.

Various agents are known to give rise to cancers. One kind of cancer agent is the virus, which is essentially a bundle of DNA held within a protein coat. When certain kinds of viruses invade certain kinds of cells, cancer follows, presumably because the DNA from the virus takes over control of the cell.

Another important kind of cancer agent is chemical. The chemicals which can cause cancer are called carcinogens, and several hundreds of them are known. In most cases, prolonged exposure to a carcinogen precedes the appearance of the cancer. A typical test to determine whether a chemical is a carcinogen is to shave the back of a mouse and apply the chemical hundreds of times over a period of many months to the mouse's skin. If the chemical is a carcinogen, the characteristic series of events will in due course follow in some of the mice: first, hyperplasia; then metaplasia; then growths or lesions composed of metaplastic cells, but still not invasive (carcinoma *in situ*); then true invasive cancer; and finally metastasis and death of the mouse. No one knows why some mice develop cancer following exposure to a carcinogen while others do not. A possible explanation is that a very common virus is also needed for cancer to develop, and that the mice which lack the virus escape the cancer despite the carcinogen.

In addition to carcinogens there are chemicals called co-carcinogens. These substances may not cause cancer even though cells are exposed to them in large amounts repeatedly over long periods. But if cells are exposed to a carcinogen also, even a very small amount of it, chronic exposure to a co-carcinogen as well may produce a much higher proportion of cancers.

There is evidence that viruses, carcinogens, and co-carcinogens can work together to produce cancers. Many years ago, for example, Dr. Peyton Rous of the Rockefeller Institute infected rabbits with a virus called the Shope papilloma virus. This virus produced hyperplasia — large wartlike growths on the rabbit — but only rarely cancer. But when the rabbits were exposed to carcinogens and co-carcinogens as well as the papilloma viruses, true cancer frequently followed. Similar results have since been secured with other combinations of viruses, carcinogens, and co-carcinogens.

Next, a word about the lungs. They are essentially devices for bringing air and blood together under conditions which permit oxygen to migrate from the air to the blood and carbon dioxide to migrate in the opposite direction from blood to air.

The air needed for this two-way transfer is carried from the windpipe or trachea to the lungs through a system of branching tubes called the bronchi. The bronchi are lined with a few layers of cells called epithelial cells. Careful studies have shown that most lung cancers originate in these cells in the bronchial linings.

Against this general background, let us return to the smoking-lung cancer problem.

CARCINOGENS AND CO-CARCINOGENS. Tobacco itself contains more than a hundred known chemical compounds, including nicotine, which will be discussed in some detail in connection with smoking and cardiovascular diseases. But the chemistry of tobacco is of very little concern to us here, since some of the substances found in the tobacco remain in the ash when the tobacco is smoked, while others are profoundly altered during the combustion process; additional compounds are also produced during combustion. What primarily concerns us, accordingly, is the composition of the cigarette smoke which results from the combustion and enters the human body.

More than 270 distinguishable chemical compounds have been identified in this smoke. Of these, at least 15 are known carcinogens; that is, they have been shown to cause cancer either in animal experiments or in observations on humans exposed to them. Here is a list of carcinogens in tobacco smoke:

Arsenious oxide	Chrysene
1:2-benzanthracene	6:7-cyclopenteno—1:2-benzanthracene
3-4-benzfluoranthene	1:2-5:6-benzanthracene
10:11-benzfluoranthene	3:4-8:9-dibenzpyrene
11:12-benzfluoranthene	3:4-9:10-dibenzpyrene
1:12-benzperylene	3-methyl-pyrene
1:2-benzpyrene	2-naphthol
3:4-benzpyrene	

In addition to this list of known carcinogens, cigarette smoke contains many substances which have not yet been tested to determine whether they are or are not carcinogens. In particular, it contains additional chemicals of the class known as polycyclic aromatic hydrocarbons. Some chemicals of this class are known carcinogens, and the remainder are accordingly suspect.

The quantity of each carcinogen identified in tobacco smoke, to be sure, is very small — in some cases exceedingly small. But here another point must be noted. Cigarette smoke also contains significant amounts of phenol, a powerful co-carcinogen. Even very small amounts of a carcinogen will produce cancer when accompanied or followed by chronic exposure to phenol. And cigarette smoke in addition contains various phenol derivatives and other substances suspected of being also co-carcinogens.

Tobacco smoke itself, when collected and concentrated, is carcinogenic, capable of producing cancer in the standard mouse-skin test. Further, it has been shown to be co-carcinogenic as well; it increases the number of cancers produced when it is applied following the application of a carcinogen.

A demonstration of this co-carcinogen effect is found in the work of Drs. Joseph A. DiPaolo and Paul R. Sheehe of the Roswell Park Memorial Institute in Buffalo, New York. They performed a standard experiment in which a specified amount of a known carcinogen, urethan, was injected into the bellies of a group of mice. Cancers appeared in due course, as expected. In addition, Drs. DiPaolo and Sheehe injected the same amount of urethan into the bellies of a second group of mice, and also painted the throats of these mice with condensed tobacco smoke five times a week for six months. These mice developed many more lung cancers than those treated with urethan alone. Indeed, the crop of cancers produced was

45

equivalent to the crop which would have been expected if the amount of urethan injected had been multiplied by 52.

Note, too, that cigarette smoke when inhaled actually reaches the cells out of which lung cancer arises. Let us review this evidence briefly.

When you take a puff of a cigarette, the smoke first enters your mouth and throat. What happens next depends on whether you inhale the smoke or not. Few pipe and cigar smokers inhale the smoke, and few of them get lung cancer. Many cigarette smokers inhale, and most cigarette smokers who get lung cancer inhale. Inhaling means that the smoke passes on down from the throat through the trachea or windpipe into the bronchial tubes.

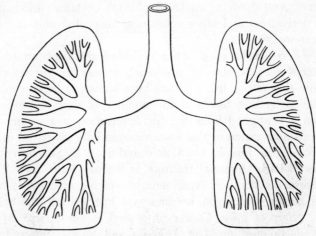

The structure of the bronchial tubes (drawn above, photographed on the facing page) resembles the branching of a tree; note that the tubes are wider just before each fork. Inhaled cigarette smoke entering these regions is slowed down by the greater width; exposure to particles in the smoke is thus greatest where the tubes are widest. Autopsy studies have shown precancerous cell changes most likely to occur here

A bronchial tube begins at the windpipe. Then it divides or forks into two tubes, and each of these forks in turn, as shown in the drawing. The structure of the tubes thus resembles in part the branching of a tree, and the tubes are therefore some-

times known as the "bronchial tree." The more deeply you inhale, the farther along the bronchial tree the smoke proceeds.

If you examine the drawing, you will note that the tube is
necessarily wider at each fork. This widening causes the air
or smoke to slow down as it enters the region of greater width
and, perhaps, to deposit any particles it may contain. The
process is much the same as that of a flowing river which
deposits its sediment as a delta where it broadens into a lake
or ocean. The exposure to the particles in the air is thus
greatest at the points where the tube is widest — and autopsy
studies of hundreds of human lungs have shown that it is in
precisely these areas of maximum exposure that precancerous
changes (hyperplasia and metaplasia of the cells) are most
likely to appear.

Thus a very plausible case can be made for a direct *causal*
(in addition to a statistical) connection between smoking and
lung cancer. Some smokers draw the smoke into their lungs
and some do not; it is mainly the smokers who inhale the
smoke who run the excess risk of lung cancer. The smoke contains carcinogens and co-carcinogens. The cells which become cancerous are those along the lining of the bronchial
tubes through which the smoke is drawn. And the lesions are
most likely to appear at the very spots, the wide places, where
exposure to the smoke is most intense. Here at the very least
is a prima facie case for a direct relationship between the
statistics reviewed earlier and events which occur in the lung.

OTHER EXPLANATIONS. Many reputable investigators feel that
this explanation of lung cancer as the result of carcinogens and
co-carcinogens found in cigarette smoke is only part of the
story. They call attention to other possible explanations.

The surface of the bronchial tubes into which smoke is
drawn is normally moist with a fluid called mucus, excreted

by cells along the surface. Further, many of the surface cells are decked with tiny whiplike fringes called cilia, which wave back and forth in such a way as to propel the mucus upward and outward. This is clearly a protective mechanism. Irritating or poisonous particles entering the lung are likely to be trapped in the mucus; and, as the mucus is propelled upward and outward by the cilia, the trapped particles are themselves ejected and the lung thus protected from them.

Cigarette smoke, however, paralyzes the ejecting action of the cilia in the bronchial tubes. As hyperplastic changes occur in the lining of the tubes, moreover, the cilia disappear altogether. Thus, inhaling smoke deprives the bronchial tubes of their normal protective mechanism. Some researchers attribute the relationship between smoking and lung cancer at least in part to this effect on the cilia rather than solely to the direct action of carcinogens and co-carcinogens.

Further, abundant evidence indicates that cigarette smoke is an irritant. No smoker who feels the irritation in his mouth or who develops a cough following smoking doubts this. Chronic, day-after-day irritation can itself evoke hyperplasia, metaplasia, and cancer in some tissues; and some investigators prefer to attribute the relationship between smoking and lung cancer to this factor of chronic irritation.

Note that the four theories based on carcinogens, co-carcinogens, paralysis and disappearance of cilia, and chronic irritation are *not* mutually exclusive or incompatible. Nature often proves far more complex than investigators initially assume. It is not at all inconceivable that two, three, or even all four of these factors may be found to play their role in the genesis of lung cancer. Cigarette smoke might initiate the damage by paralyzing the cilia, then produce hyperplasia through chronic irritation, and finally produce metaplasia and invasive metastatic cancer through both its carcinogens and its co-carcinogens. Or it may turn out that a virus is also involved, and that the smoke opens the door for the virus — or vice versa.

None of these possibilities is offered here as *the* explanation of the relationship between cigarette smoking and lung cancer. All that need be established is that they provide plausible explanations. The statistical evidence firmly establishes the relationship. The pathological and experimental evidence shows that the relationship is not so wildly improbable as to cast doubt on the credibility of the statistics.

SMOKE AND THE LUNGS OF MICE. One theme often stressed by spokesmen for the cigarette industry is the lack of experiments proving that smoking can cause lung cancer.

One such experiment can be readily imagined. Hundreds of sets of identical twins might be selected at birth. They would be brought up together in exactly the same way. At a specified age one twin in each pair would be set to smoking a specified number of cigarettes at a specified tempo to a specified butt length each day for the rest of his life, while the other twin in each pair would be monitored continuously throughout his life to make sure he never smoked a single cigarette. All twins dying would be autopsied, and a search made for lung cancer. After some 50 or 60 years, the surviving twins would be slaughtered and their lungs and bronchial tubes similarly examined. If the twins who smoked had a higher proportion of lung cancer, and if the number of lung cancers were proportional to the number of cigarettes they smoked, almost everyone except possibly the cigarette industry would agree that the smoking had caused the lung cancers.

Such an experiment is hardly feasible in a human population, of course. And even in a population of mice it raises serious difficulties. In the first place, mice breathe through their noses, not their mouths; and their nasal passages contain a series of excellent protective filters which remove particles from the air before it reaches the lungs. Thus, a mouse in a smoke-filled room gets far less of the smoke into his bronchial tubes than a smoker who inhales. Further, mice and other small animals are quite sensitive to the acute poisonous effects of nicotine or other substances in cigarette smoke. If subjected to the intensity of smoke which a human smoker draws into his lungs when he inhales, some mice keel over immediately and die; many others die soon thereafter.

The most that can be accomplished with mice and presumably other small animals is to simulate exposure to cigarette smoke very roughly comparable to that experienced in the lungs of a casual cigarette smoker.

Such an experiment has been performed by Drs. Cecilie and Rudolph Leuchtenberger and Paul F. Doolon, supported by a grant from the Tobacco Industry Research Committee. They used an inbred strain of mice closely resembling each other in genetic inheritance. Half of the mice were placed in one enclosed chamber and half in another; altogether 600 mice were used. A cigarette-smoking machine was attached to each of the chambers, and one of the machines smoked eight cigarettes a day, five days a week, month after month. The other chamber was exactly the same, and the mice in it were treated in exactly the same way except that the second cigarette-smoking machine did not actually smoke any cigarettes. The experiment thus closely duplicates the impractical experiment with human twins except that the smoke from eight cigarettes per chamber per day, inhaled through the mouse nose, was much less concentrated than the smoke which reaches the lungs of a human cigarette smoker who inhales.

After various periods of exposure in the smoke chamber, both the smoke-exposed mice and the control mice were sacrificed, and their lungs examined.

The bronchial tubes of the mice exposed to the tobacco smoke differed from the bronchial tubes of the control mice in several significant ways. First, there was more hyperplasia, or "proliferative changes" — an increased number of cells. Second, there was more metaplasia, or changes in the type of cells and in their nuclei and DNA chromosomes. Third, the Leuchtenbergers were able by subtle means to demonstrate quantitative changes in the DNA found in individual cells. Finally, whole groups of cells or lesions demonstrating these characteristics were noted in the mice exposed to smoke — the kind of lesions which might be labeled carcinoma *in situ*.

Invasive, metastatic carcinoma did not turn up during these experiments, and several reasons may be advanced for this failure of the smoke-induced lesions to take the last, fatal step. The exposure of the mouse lungs to smoke was, of course, relatively mild as compared with the exposure of the lungs of a human smoke-inhaler who gets true cancer. Also, the mouse's life is short; three years or so as compared with the 20 years or more to which a human's lung is ordinarily exposed to cigarette smoke before a cancer appears. The significant point about this experiment, at all events, is not that the metaplastic lesions in the mouse bronchial tubes failed to become invasive and metastatic, but rather that all of the precancerous changes from hyperplasia through metaplasia and the formation of lesions did appear following a relatively mild exposure of the bronchial tube lining of the mice to the smoke.

In this experiment, as in many other smoking-lung cancer experiments, the smoke did not induce uniform changes in all the mice exposed to it. Despite the fact that all of the mice came from the same inbred strain, some appeared to be strangely immune to the effects of the smoke — or, looking at the matter the other way round, some appeared to be strangely susceptible. The Leuchtenbergers and Doolon themselves suspect that a virus may prove to be the explanation of this difference in response. The mice with hyperplastic and meta-plastic changes and with lesions, they suggest, may be the ones infected with some virus or other. The virus by itself, according to this theory, rarely produces changes, and neither does tobacco smoke by itself; it may be the tobacco smoke acting on virus-infected cells, or the virus entering such smoke-damaged cells, which produces the changes noted.

"MICE ARE NOT MEN": THE HUMAN PATHOLOGICAL FINDINGS. Even though the changes typical of cancer formation can be experimentally produced in mouse bronchial tubes with tobac-co smoke, mice are not, of course, men — as spokesmen for the cigarette industry always point out in commenting on experi-ments of the kind just described. They want evidence that this also occurs in *human* bronchial tubes.

Here is the evidence.

For more than eight years four competent researchers have been engaged in a microscopic study of human lungs taken from the body at autopsy. The four are:

DR. OSCAR AUERBACH, Senior Medical Investigator at the Veterans' Ad-ministration Hospital in East Orange, New Jersey, and Associate Pro-fessor of Pathology at New York Medical College

DR. ARTHUR PURDY STOUT, Professor Emeritus of Surgery at the College of Physicians and Surgeons, Columbia University

DR. E. CUYLER HAMMOND, Director of Statistical Research, American Cancer Society (whose prospective study has already been discussed)

LAWRENCE GARFINKEL of the Statistical Research Section, American Cancer Society

The Auerbach-Stout-Hammond-Garfinkel study, financed by the American Cancer Society, comes closer than any other project except the statistical studies to nailing the relationship between smoking and lung cancer. In the course of the project more than 100,000 separate slides containing cells from the bronchial tubes of 1,522 men and women were examined under the microscope — a tremendous undertaking. Dr. Auerbach examined every one of the 100,000 slides to assure uniformity of judgment. Dr. Stout checked Dr. Auerbach's findings by re-examining a selection of slides to see if he reached the same conclusions. Some of the tissue examined came from non-smokers, some from light smokers, heavy smokers, and ex-smokers. All of the 1,522 patients had died of causes other than lung cancer. Relatives were interviewed to ascertain the smoking history of the men whose lungs were examined; the interviewers were not, of course, informed of the microscopic findings at any time, and, to avoid bias, Drs. Auerbach and Stout were not informed of the smoking histories until after they had examined the slides. Each slide was identified only by a serial number selected at random, so that if any errors were made in reading the slides, they would be random errors, affecting slides from the lungs of non-smokers along with those from the lungs of smokers.

The findings from this human study closely parallel the mouse findings of the Leuchtenbergers, but go at least one important step farther.

Like the Leuchtenberger study, the Auerbach study found each step in the cancer process clearly identifiable — hyperplasia, or excessive number of cells; metaplasia, or characteristic changes in the cells and in their nuclei; and the formation of lesions composed entirely of such cells (this is the stage of carcinoma in situ).

The Auerbach study established that the precancerous changes were most likely to occur at the places where the bronchial tubes forked — that is, at precisely the places where the exposure to the smoke is greatest (see page 46).

The study noted occasional cases of hyperplasia and metaplasia among men and women who had never smoked. This is in line with the statistical finding that lung cancer does occur occasionally in non-smokers.

The proportion of hyperplasia, metaplasia, and cells with atypical nuclei, however, was very much higher among cigarette smokers than among non-smokers. Further, carcinoma *in situ*, strictly defined, was found only among smokers. Cigar and pipe smokers had more precancerous lesions than non-smokers, but fewer than cigarette smokers (see pages 74-75).

The number of places in the bronchial tubes showing hyperplasia, metaplasia, and carcinoma *in situ* was proportional to the amount of smoking. The heavy smokers — those who smoked a pack a day or more — had the largest number of these precancerous changes in their lungs. Indeed, the bronchial linings of heavy smokers who died of causes other than lung cancer closely resembled in almost every respect the lungs of lung cancer victims. In some cases, ominously enough, actual invasive cancers were found — small cancers which had not yet made known their presence when death ensued from other causes.

The Auerbach-Stout-Hammond-Garfinkel data can be interpreted in several ways. They are consistent with the carcinogen theory, the co-carcinogen theory, and the chronic irritation theory. They are even consistent with the virus theory, for it may be a virus which ultimately determines whether or not the changes noted will progress from one stage to another. And Dr. Hammond points to still another interpretation.

Bronchial lining cells, he suggests, may develop hyperplasia and metaplasia spontaneously, without any external agent causing these changes. This is shown by the fact that some non-smokers develop these changes, and even progress to lung cancer. The environment in the normal lung, however, favors the survival and multiplication of normal cells in their competition with the precancerous cells; this would explain why so few of the non-smokers with abnormal cells in their lungs go on to develop lung cancer.

In the lung of the cigarette inhaler the environment is very different. The cilia are paralyzed; they disappear; the cells are exposed to many chemicals which affect their chances of survival. Under the altered conditions introduced by the inhaling of cigarette smoke, Dr. Hammond suggests, the metaplastic cells may gain some important competitive advantage over the normal cells. They multiply, and the cancer results from this competitive advantage.

All competent researchers in this area agree that the full story is not yet available. Much more research is urgently needed. But already we know that cigarette smoke as a "cause" of lung cancer is not a remote or implausible suggestion to be dismissed out of hand. On the contrary, it is a highly plausible and reasonable suggestion. It is strictly in line with the experimental and pathological evidence assembled to date. Not only one but several plausible descriptions of the way in which cigarette smoke might "cause" cancer can be presented: the carcinogen theory; the co-carcinogen theory; the chronic irritation theory; the cilia paralysis and destruction theory; Hammond's recent altered-environment theory; or any combination of these, or a combination of these with the virus theory.

Any one of these approaches would be enough to show the plausibility of the conclusion that cigarette smoking *can* cause cancer. When combined with the statistical evidence that cigarette smoking *does* cause cancer, there is simply no remaining room for reasonable doubt.

CHAPTER 4
Lung Cancer: A Summing Up

THE ATTENTIVE READER will no doubt by now have noted that the word "cause" has been used only rarely in this presentation, and then generally in quotation marks. For though most laymen, if asked, would no doubt assure you that they know what the word "cause" means, there are considerable difficulties in defining it precisely — and even greater difficulties in determining whether a particular set of facts does or does not fit the chosen definitions of "cause" and "effect." Philosophers, logicians, and scientists have thought much and debated more on the meaning and applicability of these terms.

The difficulties inherent in these concepts, moreover, have been obfuscated recently by those whose main aim seems to be to make sure that the cigarette smoking-lung cancer relationship shall *not* be described as a cause-and-effect relationship. This can be done by setting up definitions of cause and effect so stringent that nothing can ever be shown to be the cause of anything else. This saves cigarette smoking from being labeled a cause of lung cancer, of course; but it also requires the introduction of some new term for the relationship.

We propose to detour around this debate over words almost altogether, and to consider instead at this point the two questions which should really interest laymen when they consider whether smoking "causes" cancer.

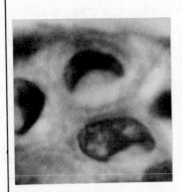
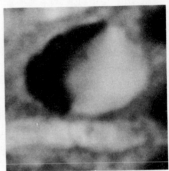

Disintegrating cell nuclei from the lungs of an
ex-smoker as observed by the Auerbach-Stout-
Hammond-Garfinkel group (see pages 60-61)

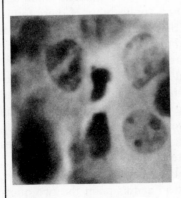
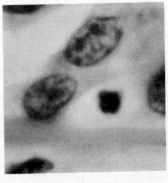

The first practical question the layman should bear in mind is quite simply, "If I start smoking cigarettes, will my chances of dying of lung cancer go up significantly?" The answer is Yes.

The other practical question is for men and women who already smoke cigarettes: "If I stop smoking them, will my chances of getting lung cancer go down?" The answer is again Yes.

Statistical evidence on the latter score comes from the prospective studies reviewed earlier. The Doll and Hill study of deaths among British physicians, for example, produced the following data:

	LUNG CANCER DEATHS PER 100,000 MAN-YEARS
Non-smokers	10
Ex-smokers who gave up smoking 10 years or more before study began	24
Ex-smokers who gave up smoking 1 to 10 years before study began	64
Smokers who continued to smoke	112

Clearly the men who stopped smoking ran a smaller risk than those who continued to smoke, and the risk diminished further after a decade of non-smoking.

The Hammond-Horn prospective study of American smokers and non-smokers, because it dealt with a larger study population, was able to display this effect separately among both heavy and light cigarette smokers.

Among the heavy smokers (a pack a day or more) the figures were as follows:

	LUNG CANCER DEATHS PER 100,000 MAN-YEARS
Non-smokers	3
Ex-smokers who gave up smoking 10 years or more before study began	61
Ex-smokers who gave up smoking 1 to 10 years before study began	78
Smokers who continued to smoke	158

Among the light smokers (less than a pack a day) the effect of stopping was quite similar:

	LUNG CANCER DEATHS PER 100,000 MAN-YEARS
Non-smokers	3
Ex-smokers who gave up smoking 10 years or more before study began	8
Ex-smokers who gave up smoking 1 to 10 years before study began	36
Smokers who continued to smoke	58

The mouse-lung experiments of the Leuchtenbergers fully confirm the statistical findings in this respect. They examined some mice immediately after a series of exposures in the smoke chamber, and other mice after several months of "recovery" in a smoke-free chamber. The mice allowed to recover showed more changes in their lungs than those never exposed to smoke, but fewer than the mice examined immediately. The findings indicate that the lesions caused by the smoking — at least up to the final, fatal change to invasive and metastatic carcinoma — are reversible, and that during a period of recovery following smoke exposure the lesions tend to disappear.

Next, the human-lung observations of the Auerbach-Stout-Hammond-Garfinkel group fully confirm both the statistical and the experimental evidence. These researchers compared tissues taken from the lungs of 72 ex-smokers with tissues taken from the lungs of 72 non-smokers and 72 smokers who continued to smoke until lung cancer was diagnosed. The three groups were matched for age, occupational status, and urban-or-rural residence. Metaplastic cells with altered nuclei were found in 1.2 per cent of the slides from the lungs of non-smokers, as compared with 6.0 per cent for ex-smokers — and 93.2 per cent for current smokers!

Further, the Auerbach group found in the lungs of ex-smokers a kind of cell that they had never seen anywhere else, in either smokers or non-smokers. These cells had a contracted nucleus and seemed to be dying; the Auerbach group named them "disintegrating cells." The suggestion is that they represent precancerous cells which are dying out in ex-smokers instead of reproducing and multiplying. The Auerbach group concludes:

"We feel that the findings of an increase in the number of cells with atypical nuclei following exposure to cigarette smoke, and a decrease in such cells with cessation of smoking, provides a reasonable explanation for the now well-established relationship between cigarette smoking and lung cancer."

These data, of course, should be of the greatest practical interest to men and women who are wondering whether or not they should stop smoking cigarettes. But, in addition, they have overwhelming theoretical significance, as a moment's thought will show.

One objection sometimes raised to the smoking-lung cancer

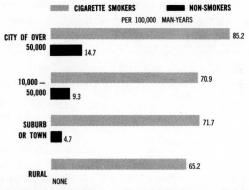

DEATH RATES from well-established cases of lung cancer for cigarette smokers vs. non-smokers (meaning men who never at any time smoked regularly) in urban and rural areas. Adenocarcinoma cases, less linked to smoking than other kinds, are not included

theory is the possibility that some other factor associated with smoking — call it once more the X-factor — may be responsible for the lung cancer. As noted earlier, this suppositious factor would have at least the following curious characteristics:

Smokers must have this factor and non-smokers must lack it.

Pipe and cigar smokers must have less of it than cigarette smokers.

Seventh Day Adventists must lack this factor.

To this unlikely list must now be added a fourth implausible characteristic of the hypothetical X-factor; it must occasionally disappear in men who have had it for years or even decades — and this disappearance must occur only among men who stop smoking!

THE EXPERTS SPEAK OUT. As the evidence above — and great masses of additional evidence from many other sources — has accumulated, more and more public bodies in the United States and in other countries have spoken out on the issue, usually after reviewing the evidence in some detail. A summary of the conclusions and recommendations of such bodies is presented below in chronological order.

"Since the presently available evidence indicates an association between smoking and lung cancer, be it resolved that the American Cancer Society and the U.S. Public Health Service ... devise and pursue public health education and other measures designed to control the rising incidence of lung cancer especially as it relates to cigarette smoking."
  Resolution adopted by the Third National Cancer Conference (September 11, 1954)

"Resolved, that there is sufficient evidence available of a relationship between smoking and lung cancer to justify advising the public to stop smoking cigarettes as a means of eventually lowering the incidence and to advise the youth of America to ponder well the question whether the risk entailed is worth the pleasure derived."
  Resolution of the Public Health Cancer Association (October 11, 1954)

"Resolved, that the American Cancer Society emphasize to the American people that the presently available evidence indicates an association between smoking, particularly cigarette smoking, and lung cancer, and to a lesser degree other forms of cancer...."

Resolution adopted by the American Cancer Society (October 22, 1954)

"The sum total of scientific evidence establishes beyond reasonable doubt that cigarette smoking is a causative factor in the rapidly increasing incidence of human epidermoid cancer of the lung. The evidence of a cause-effect relationship is adequate for considering the initiation of public health measures."

Joint Report of the Seven-Man Study Group on Smoking and Health, representing the American Cancer Society, the American Heart Association, The National Cancer Institute, and the National Heart Institute (March 6, 1957)

"The [Netherlands] Government has noticed with apprehension the rapid increase in lung cancer which has taken place during the last decades.... The Government has consulted experts. . . . These have given as their opinion that, although the proof of a causal relationship ... understandably cannot be furnished, there are no counter arguments against the assumption of such a relationship. If the above-mentioned increase continues at the same pace, the frequency of lung cancer in the following generation of adults will be alarmingly great. It is, therefore, [clear] that today's youth would do well not to make a habit of smoking, particularly of cigarettes."

Health Council of The Netherlands (March 9, 1957)

"Evidence from many investigations in different countries indicates that a major part of the increase [in lung cancer] is associated with tobacco smoking, particularly in the form of cigarettes. In the opinion of the Council, the most reasonable interpretation of this evidence is that the relationship is one of direct cause and effect."

Medical Research Council of Great Britain (June 29, 1957)

"... the weight of the evidence is increasingly pointing in one direction: that excessive smoking is one of the causative factors in lung cancer."

Surgeon General of the U.S. Public Health Service (September, 1957)

"... it is the view of the [Research] Council [of Sweden] that collective completed investigations indicate that substances in tobacco smoke con-

63

stitute, in all probability, an essential factor in the occurrence of certain types of lung cancer."
"Statement to the King on ... Effects of Tobacco Smoking" (May 12, 1958)

"There is now no reasonable doubt on the part of authoritative health agencies concerned with cancer that the use of tobacco acts in some way to increase the chances of developing lung cancer to a significant degree."
Commissioner of Health, New York State (August 22, 1958)

"... the weight of evidence with regard to cigarette smoking as a cause of lung cancer is now so great that the Department [of Public Health of the State of California] must bring the matter to the attention of the public."
Director of California State Department of Public Health (June 1, 1959)

"Whereas, lung cancer is a rapidly increasing fatal disease which now kills more than 25,000 people in the United States each year and if present trends continue will claim the lives of more than 1,000,000 present school children in this country before they reach the age of 70 years, and
"Whereas, scientific evidence has established that excessive cigarette smoking is a major factor in the disease, and
"Whereas, public health officials in the United States and many other countries have pointed out the relationship between cigarette smoking and lung cancer, therefore be it
"Resolved, that the American Public Health Association call upon health authorities to undertake a broad educational effort, especially among young people, to prevent cigarette smoking. . . ."
Resolution Adopted by American Public Health Association (October 21, 1959)

"The Study Group [of the World Health Organization] unanimously agreed that ... the sum total of the evidence available today was reasonably interpreted as indicating that cigarette smoking is a major causative factor in the increasing incidence of human carcinoma of the lung."
Report of a WHO Study Group on the Epidemiology of Cancer of the Lung (November 20, 1959)

"The weight of evidence at present implicates smoking as the principal etiological factor in the increased incidence of lung cancer."
Surgeon General of the U.S. Public Health Service (November 28, 1959)

"The Board [of Directors of the American Cancer Society] now believes that it has a . . . responsibility . . . to state that in its judgment the clinical, epidemiological, experimental, chemical, and pathologic evidence . . . indicates beyond reasonable doubt that cigarette smoking is the major cause of the unprecedented increase in lung cancer."
Statement by the American Cancer Society (January 21, 1960)

"The National Tuberculosis Association warns all persons that —

there is an alarming increase in deaths from lung cancer

cigarette smoking is a major cause of lung cancer

the risk of lung cancer increases with the number of cigarettes smoked

giving up smoking reduces the risk of lung cancer

. . . cigarette smoking is a factor in such crippling lung diseases as chronic bronchitis and emphysema. . . ."
Statement of the National Tuberculosis Association (February 27, 1960)

"The strong statistical association between smoking, especially of cigarettes, and lung cancer is most simply explained on a causal basis. This is supported by compatible, though not conclusive laboratory evidence, namely (a) the presence of several substances known to be capable of producing cancer in tobacco smoke; (b) the production of cancer of the skin in animals by repeated application of tobacco tar; and (c) the finding, in the bronchial epithelium of smokers, of microscopic changes of the kind which may precede development of cancer. The conclusion that smoking is an important cause of lung cancer implies that if the habit ceased, the death rate from lung cancer would eventually fall to a fraction, perhaps to one fifth, or even, among men, to one tenth of the present level."
Report of the Royal College of Physicians of London (March 7, 1962)

"The weight of scientific evidence . . . demonstrates that cigarette smoking is a major cause of the increase in cancer of the lung. It is clear that an individual's risk to lung cancer rises in relation to the number of cigarettes smoked. Everyone should be aware of these conclusions because of their importance to health."
Surgeon General of the U.S. Public Health Service (April, 1962)

"The weight of scientific evidence distinctly indicates that cigarette smoking and the inhalation of other atmospheric pollutants have an association relationship which strongly suggests a causal connection with chronic bronchitis, pulmonary emphysema, cor pulmonale, cardiovascular diseases, and cancer of the lung.

65

"The College urges its members and the medical profession in general to intensify their educational campaign directed toward the public, and the youth in particular, relative to the hazards of smoking."

Boards of Regents of the American College of Chest Physicians (June 22, 1962)

". . . the Grand Council and Board of Directors of the Canadian Cancer Society desire to see a broad programme of public education on the problem of lung cancer and smoking initiated as early as expedient through the media of the Canadian Cancer Society, the Canadian Medical Association, L'Association des Medecins de Langue Francaise du Canada and such other organizations dealing in matters of public health as may be interested."

Statement by the Canadian Cancer Society (October, 1962)

As this volume went to press, a 1963 Surgeon General's Advisory Committee on Smoking and Health was again reviewing the evidence, this time on a broader scale and with reference to cardiovascular, respiratory, and other conditions as well as cancer. A preliminary report is expected before the end of the year (see page 205).

CIGARETTE SMOKING IS NOT THE ONLY "CAUSE." While the evidence accumulated to date, and the conclusions drawn from the evidence by competent, impartial public bodies, leaves no reasonable room for doubt that cigarette smoking causes lung cancer in the usual meaning of the word "cause," it certainly does not follow that cigarette smoking is the only cause or the only factor in lung cancer.

Heredity, for example, may play a role in the disease. There are studies suggesting that the close relatives of a lung cancer patient are somewhat more likely to contract the disease than others. But the hereditary factor is mild, indeed barely discernible, as compared with the overwhelming impact of the cigarette-smoking factor.

Viruses, as we have seen, may somehow or other be involved in the causation of lung cancer. They may explain, for example, why some heavy smokers get lung cancer while others do not. But virus-lung cancer evidence, if it were to become available later on, would in no way mitigate the direct, overwhelming impact of cigarette smoking.

Air pollution is quite probably also a factor in lung cancer. Indeed, a quite convincing case can be made out for such a relationship, including the known presence of carcinogens and co-carcinogens in the polluted air of our cities. A detailed review of this case falls outside the scope of this book on *smoking* and the public interest. The prospective studies do show, however, that of the two factors, cigarette smoking is by far the more significant. The possibility has not been ruled out that smoking and air pollution may have a combined effect which is greater than either factor considered separately.

... AND LUNG CANCER IS NOT INEVITABLE. Finally, the statistics do not point to an inevitable death from lung cancer for all cigarette smokers. Even among those who smoke two packs or more a day from boyhood to old age, eight or nine out of ten will die of something else. The difficulty is that no one can tell in advance *which* smokers will escape. The most that can be said is that the risk of lung cancer for cigarette smokers as a group is enormously increased, and is directly proportional to the amount smoked.

CHAPTER 5
"Death from All Causes"

IN MOVING from lung cancer to the many other diseases with which heavy cigarette smoking may also be associated, we are moving from territory which has been well mapped to an area where even some of the preliminary explorations have not as yet been completed. The epidemiological, pathological, and experimental evidence all fit neatly together in lung cancer research, as we have seen. There are also some strikingly good fits with respect to other diseases; and, as in the case of lung cancer, there is a striking lack of negative evidence pointing toward the innocence of smoking. Still, the data are not yet adequate to present the kind of detailed case against smoking with respect to other diseases that could be presented with respect to lung cancer.

One reason for this lag is the relative newness of the statistical evidence linking smoking to a wide range of diseases. The retrospective studies linking smoking with lung cancer during the 1940s and early 1950s made a very convincing case for a causal relationship, and therefore stimulated pathological and laboratory studies which have confirmed the statistical findings. But these retrospective studies by their very nature could not reveal the link between smoking and other diseases, for they started with groups of lung cancer victims and were therefore concerned almost solely with this one disease.

The subsequent prospective studies, in contrast, started with groups of presumably healthy smokers and non-smokers. These studies were therefore able to determine during the years of follow-up not only whether there was an increased incidence of lung cancer among the smokers but also whether any other diseases were found more frequently among smokers than among non-smokers.

When the results of the prospective studies were examined from this broad point of view, they demonstrated — no doubt to the astonishment of some of the researchers themselves — that lung cancer was in fact merely one of the lesser aftermaths of heavy cigarette smoking. Indeed, it turned out that lung cancer accounted for only about one seventh of the excess deaths among smokers. Excess deaths from such conditions as the cardiovascular diseases, the lung diseases other than cancer, and cancers other than lung cancer turned out to bulk far larger in combination than excess deaths from lung cancer.

The American Cancer Society has presented figures, based on its own and other studies, in terms of the "death expectancy" of men aged 35:

PERCENTAGE OF AMERICAN MEN AGED 35 WHO MAY BE EXPECTED TO DIE BEFORE THE AGE OF 65

Non-smokers	23%
Cigar and pipe smokers	25%
Cigarette smokers:	
Less than 1/2 pack a day	27%
1/2 to 1 pack a day	34%
1 to 2 packs a day	38%
2 or more packs a day	41%

The prospective studies show further that the differential between smokers and non-smokers is particularly noticeable in the earlier age groups. Here, for example, are age-group death rates published by the Royal College of Physicians, based on the Doll-Hill study of smokers and non-smokers among English physicians:

DEATH RATES FROM ALL CAUSES PER 1,000 MEN PER YEAR

AGE	NON-SMOKERS	SMOKERS OF 25 OR MORE CIGARETTES PER DAY
35-44	1.1	4.4
45-54	3.7	10.2
55-64	12.0	25.6
65-74	31.7	60.0

Even among men past 65, heavy cigarette smoking was associated with a doubling of the death rate; but among men aged 35 to 44, the death rate was quadrupled.

These death rates among smokers are perhaps the least controversial of all the findings to date. For with respect to any particular disease there is always the possibility, however remote, that mistaken diagnosis and other conceivable errors may cast doubt on the statistics. But death is easily diagnosed.

It is conceivable, of course, that smoking is not the "cause" of the excess deaths, but that some other factor associated with smoking — our old friend the X-factor, for example — may be responsible. Once again, however, the X-factor hypothesis loses plausibility when the more detailed figures are examined. Here, for example, are some detailed figures from the Hammond-Horn study. The death rate of non-smokers is pegged at 1.00, and the comparative death rates for other groups are then presented:

Non-smokers	1.00
Smokers who smoke only a pipe	1.12
Smokers who smoke only cigars	1.22
Smokers who smoked a pack of cigarettes a day or more, but who stopped smoking 10 years or more before the study began	1.50
Smokers who smoked a pack of cigarettes a day or more, and who stopped smoking from 1 to 10 years before the study began	1.82
Smokers who continued to smoke two packs or more a day	2.23

To explain away these figures by means of an X-factor, we must assume not only (1) that this hypothetical factor is associated with smoking, and (2) that it causes lung cancer, but also (3) that cigarette smokers have more of it than pipe or cigar smokers, (4) that ex-smokers have less of it than continuing smokers, and (5) that ex-smokers who stopped smoking early have less of it than ex-smokers who stopped later on. Such an X-factor surely invites disbelief. A much simpler and more rational explanation attributes the excess deaths to the cigarette smoking directly. In some way or other, we may suppose for the moment, smoking exerts a generally handicapping effect on the human organism, so that humans who have been smoking heavily for many years are more likely to die from almost any disease than non-smokers of the same age under the same conditions.

THE HANDICAPPING EFFECT. There are several well-known examples of factors which produce such a generalized effect. One dramatic example was the Great London Smog of 1952 (and a similar smog in 1962). During one week of the 1952 smog, the London death rate rose by 250 per cent; several thousand excess deaths were recorded. Some of these excess deaths were attributed on the death certificates to pneumonia, influenza, bronchitis, asthma, and emphysema — all lung conditions. Many were attributed to various forms of heart and circulatory disease, and some to diseases with only a remote relationship to the smog.

Again, the recurrent influenza epidemics which sweep through this and other countries are routinely associated not only with an increased death rate from influenza but also with an increase in deaths attributed to many other diseases.

On reflection, these non-specific effects of smogs and flu epidemics are plausible enough. Death occurs, after all, when the heart stops beating and the lungs stop breathing. Anything which puts an added stress on heart or lungs, or which impairs their efficiency, might be expected to tip the scales toward death rather than survival in a wide range of circumstances. When death occurs, it is quite properly attributed to the underlying disease or diseases; but the precipitating role of the smog or flu attack must nevertheless be recognized.

Dr. Hammond has suggested that smoking, too, may have a generalized effect of this kind on the death rate from all causes combined.

Every cell in the human body, Dr. Hammond points out, requires oxygen. The cells get their oxygen from the blood stream. The blood, in turn, gets its oxygen as it circulates through the lungs. The oxygen-laden air you inhale passes down the windpipe into the bronchial tubes, as described earlier, and then flows on into tiny sacs or chambers called alveoli. Each alveolus is separated from its neighbors by membranes called septa. Blood is brought into this labyrinth by small arteries, and flows through the septa in even smaller vessels called arterioles. Oxygen seeps from the air in the alveoli through the septa and the walls of the arterioles into the blood, and carbon dioxide is returned from the blood to the air. Survival is dependent on the continuous oxygenation of the blood by the alveoli in this way.

Under ordinary circumstances, the lungs have a tremendous excess capacity for oxygenating the blood. If one lung is removed altogether, the other can do the work. A runner who covers a mile in four minutes requires a tremendous increase in oxygen, yet his lungs are able to supply it.

But this excess lung capacity has a limit, and there is evidence that in many life-threatening conditions the limit is significant in determining death or survival. Knowing this, physicians commonly enrich the air with oxygen for patients in crisis — thus recognizing the crucial role of oxygenation for survival when things are otherwise nip-and-tuck.

Impairment of lung function, moreover, might be expected to have an effect on the heart as well, requiring the heart to pump more blood in order to meet the oxygen needs of the body. From this point of view the heart and lungs may be considered as a single heart-lung machine, working together to supply the body with oxygen. If it could be shown that cigarette smoking has an adverse effect on this heart-lung machine, lowering its oxygenating efficiency in the way the Great London Smog of 1952 did or a flu attack does, we would have at hand a plausible explanation for the higher death rates from all causes combined as shown in the prospective studies.

This is precisely what recent post-mortem studies of human lungs have shown.

The new studies have been reported by the same Auerbach-Stout-Hammond-Garfinkel team whose studies of bronchial tubes were reported earlier. Once again, the researchers examined lungs from smokers and non-smokers alike who died from various causes. The studies were "blind" in the sense that the pathologists who examined the tissues were not told whether they came from the lungs of smokers or non-smokers. These studies revealed four significant differences between the lungs of non-smokers and of heavy cigarette smokers. All four kinds of change in the lung tissue appear to be of a kind which might impair the exchange of oxygen between the air and the blood in the lungs — thus lowering the efficiency of the whole heart-lung machine. Let us review these changes in turn.

THICKENING OF THE WALLS OF THE SMALL ARTERIES. When the wall of an artery is thickened, the interior space or lumen of the artery is reduced, and less blood can therefore flow through at a given speed — or the heart action must be increased to

73

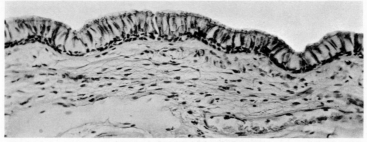

Normal bronchial epithelium

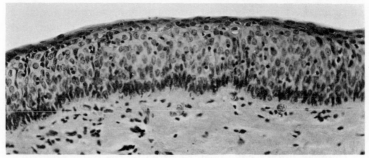

Squamous metaplasia (flattening of cells on the surface). Cilia are absent. This condition, as found in the Auerbach study, was much higher among smokers than among non-smokers

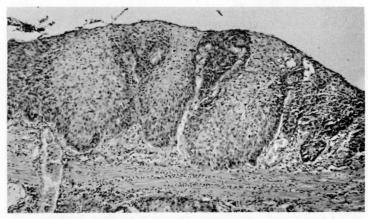

Greatly thickened epithelium showing a loss of cilia. There is disorientation and loss of layering of cells. This is carcinoma *in situ,* found only among smokers.

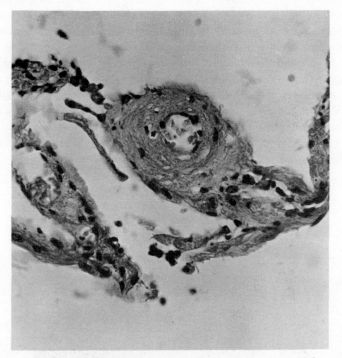

Greatly thickened arteriole surrounded by thickened alveolar septa. This thickening appears in few non-smokers, in
most cigarette smokers by the age of 65, and in all two-
packs-a-day smokers by the age of 70

supply the same amount of blood per minute. There is some slight or moderate thickening of these small arteries in some old men, Dr. Auerbach and his associates report, even among non-smokers. But a *high degree of thickening* is never noted among non-smokers, even among men past 65. Among smokers, in contrast, a high degree of thickening makes its appearance quite early; and by the age of 70 all heavy cigarette smokers show a high degree of thickening.

A second pathological change reported by the Auerbach group is an increased THICKENING OF THE WALLS OF THE TINY ARTERIOLES. This thickening, too, appears in few non-smokers, in most cigarette smokers by the age of 65, and in all two-packs-a-day smokers by the age of 70.

A third type of change found frequently in the lungs of heavy smokers is a THICKENING OR "FIBROSIS" OF THE SEPTA OR

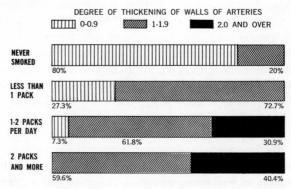

LUNG CHANGES found at autopsy in the Auerbach study (see text) varied with amount of cigarette smoking. Thickening of the walls of the lung arterioles, fibrosis, and rupturing of the walls of the lung alveoli also followed approximately the pattern shown above (see photos on pages 74-75)

WALLS OF THE ALVEOLI. Like the thickening of the arterioles, this fibrosis of the septa may also impair the exchange of oxygen between air and blood. The elasticity of the lungs, and therefore their ability to inhale and exhale, is also impaired by these changes. This fibrosis of the alveolar septa is similarly related to amounts smoked and to age.

Finally, Dr. Auerbach and his associates report ACTUAL RUPTURING OF THE SEPTA, and thus destruction of the air-containing ability of the alveoli. This also impairs the elasticity of the lung. Occasional septa may be ruptured in anybody's lungs; but, as in the case of other changes, a high degree of rupturing is noted solely in the lungs of smokers.

Much more research will be needed to confirm these findings and to determine their significance. But, once again, combining the evidence greatly increases the significance of the individual studies.

Smoking has a number of other well-established systemic effects which warrant mention here. One is an effect on the adrenal glands and the sympathetic nerve endings which causes them to release into the blood stream hormones called catecholamines, of which adrenalin and noradrenalin are the best known. These hormones have specific effects on the heart and blood vessels, including perhaps the blood vessels in the lungs. Further, smoking causes a release of catecholamines stored within the heart muscle itself. In addition, smoking causes the hypothalamic-pituitary system to release an antidiuretic hormone, probably pitressin, which has cardiovascular effects as well as an effect on the kidneys. The distribution of serotonin, a substance with important actions both in the brain and in the cardiovascular system, may also be affected by smoking. Finally, smoke contains carbon monoxide and other physiologically significant gases.

Researches on these subtle hormone and gaseous effects of

smoking on the heart-lung mechanism or on other essential organ-systems has barely begun. The extent to which they may tip the scales toward death rather than survival in times of physiological crisis — either singly, or in combination, or along with the lung deterioration described by the Auerbach group — is simply not known.

But we need not rely either on the evidence of lung deterioration or on little-understood effects of hormones or gases to explain the excess death rates among heavy cigarette smokers. An alternative approach is to consider in turn each of the diseases found to be associated with smoking in the prospective studies, and to ask the same question with respect to each disease individually: How can its association with cigarette smoking be explained? This is the task of the next chapter.

CHAPTER 6
Smoking and Other Diseases

THE PROSPECTIVE STUDIES (see page 33) showed, as we have seen, that cigarette smokers are more likely than non-smokers to die not only of lung cancer but also of other cancers, cardiovascular diseases, and various miscellaneous conditions. One way to present these relationships is in terms of relative death rates. The death rate among non-smokers is arbitrarily set at 1.00, and the death rates among smokers are then presented as a multiple of 1.00. Thus a relative death rate of 1.30 for strokes means that death from strokes was 30% more common among smokers than among non-smokers in the group studied during the period of the study.

The figures below show the relative death rates for regular cigarette smokers (light, moderate, and heavy smokers combined) in the Hammond-Horn study which we reviewed earlier (other studies have yielded reasonably comparable results):

Lung cancer	10.7
Cancer at other sites directly exposed to the smoke (lips, mouth, tongue, larynx, pharynx, esophagus)	5.1
Gastric and duodenal ulcer	4.0
Aneurysm and Buerger's disease	3.0
Pulmonary disease except cancer (bronchitis, emphysema, influenza, tuberculosis)	2.8
Cancer of the bladder	2.0
Cirrhosis of the liver	1.9

Coronary artery disease	1.7
Cancer at other sites	1.4
Cerebral vascular lesions (strokes)	1.3

This listing tends to overestimate the importance of smoking in some respects and to underestimate its importance in others. Cancer of the esophagus, for example, is relatively rare. Even if the death rate among smokers were 100 times higher than among non-smokers, the number of esophageal cancer deaths caused by smoking would remain very small.

A second way of presenting the figures takes this factor into account. Based on the Hammond-Horn study, it begins with this simple calculation:

Total deaths from all causes among regular cigarette smokers in the study	7,316
Deaths expected if smokers had the same death rate as non-smokers	4,651
Excess deaths experienced among cigarette smokers	2,665

These 2,665 excess deaths are next taken as 100 per cent, and the question is asked: What proportion of these excess deaths is attributable to each disease? The Hammond-Horn answer is as follows:

Coronary artery disease	52.1%	(1,388 excess deaths)
Lung cancer	13.5%	(360 excess deaths)
Cancer at sites not directly exposed to smoke	10.7%	(286 excess deaths)
Pulmonary disease except cancer (bronchitis, emphysema, influenza, tuberculosis, etc.)	5.6%	(150 excess deaths)
Cerebral vascular lesions (strokes)	4.8%	(128 excess deaths)
Gastric and duodenal ulcer	2.8%	(75 excess deaths)
Cancer at sites directly exposed to smoke (lips, mouth, tongue, etc.)	2.7%	(73 excess deaths)
Aneurysm and Buerger's disease	2.1%	(57 excess deaths)
Cirrhosis of the liver	1.5%	(40 excess deaths)
All other causes of death	4.2%	(108 excess deaths)
TOTAL	100.0%	(2,665 excess deaths)

For each of these diseases or groups of diseases (other than lung cancer), the question will now be asked separately: *What is the nature of its relationship with smoking?*

■ CORONARY ARTERY DISEASE. This is by far the major cause of excess deaths among cigarette smokers, accounting in the United States for more excess deaths than all the other diseases, including lung cancer, added together.

Yet coronary artery disease is also the commonest cause of death among non-smokers, and would no doubt continue to be the commonest cause if smoking were discontinued altogether. In part for this reason, the relationship between smoking and coronary artery disease is much the most hotly debated of all the smoking relationships revealed by the prospective studies.

One school of thought denies that there is any specific causal relationship between smoking and coronary artery disease. Rather, it is suggested, smoking increases a smoker's vulnerability to death from many causes (as described in Chapter 5), and excess deaths from coronary artery disease among cigarette smokers are simply an exemplification of this general handicapping effect. This is certainly a reasonable point of view. It is hardly a comforting one for smokers, however. The 1,388 smokers who died "excess deaths" from coronary artery disease in the group studied by Hammond and Horn are really dead. It is of little importance to them whether their deaths were due to a general handicapping effect or to the specific effect of smoking on the progress of their coronary artery disease.

Other researchers are seeking direct and specific relationships between smoking and coronary artery disease. To appreciate their theories, a brief review of the nature of this disease may prove useful.

Quite early in life, most American males begin to develop a condition called atherosclerosis. One factor in atherosclerosis is the deposit of fatty substances (mostly cholesterol) in the linings of the arteries. For many years these deposits do no apparent harm. But, as they grow in size and number, they increasingly impede the flow of blood through the arteries. Further, the linings of the arteries become roughened by the fatty deposits, and this roughening increases the likelihood that a blood clot or thrombus may form, blocking the artery altogether — a condition called thrombosis.

Among the arteries most likely to develop these fatty deposits and roughening are the coronary arteries, whose function is to supply blood to the heart muscle itself. If the coronary arteries do not supply sufficient blood, ischemic heart disease may follow. A mild form of this disease, due to inadequate oxygen supply to the heart muscle, is known as angina pectoris. The most serious form is myocardial infarction, or death of some part of the heart muscle due to a shutting off of the blood supply to that part. There are other variants which need not be described here. All are included within the general term, coronary artery disease.

There are clearly many ways in which smoking might affect either the onset or the ultimate course of this group of conditions. Let us consider them one by one.

Smoking might affect the level of fats or fatty acids in the blood, and thus lead to the development of those fatty deposits in the arteries. Some studies have shown such an effect. Other studies, in contrast, have failed to demonstrate higher levels of cholesterol in the blood of smokers. The verdict: "Not proved."

Again, smoking might affect the clotting mechanism of the blood, so that smokers would be more likely to suffer from blockage of the coronary arteries — coronary thrombosis — and thus from myocardial infarction. Some studies have suggested such an effect. But blood-clotting studies are as yet far from decisive. Again the verdict is: "Not proved."

The amount of blood the heart muscle needs is dependent on the work it must do. Anything which increases the heart's workload may therefore predispose to ischemic heart disease, especially if the coronary arteries are unable to adjust to the extra workload and deliver more blood to the heart. The lung changes reported in the Auerbach-Stout-Hammond-Garfinkel studies suggest that the hearts of heavy cigarette smokers are subjected to heavier workloads. But the verdict so far must again be: "Not proved."

The normal heart and circulatory systems respond to excess workloads by increasing the flow of blood through the coronary arteries to the heart muscle. Some studies suggest that in smokers with coronary artery disease, this automatic adjustment of blood flow to increased needs is impaired. But this relationship, too, must at present be labelled: "Not proved."

Finally, the subtle hormonal changes such as the release of catecholamines by the adrenal glands, sympathetic nerve endings, and heart muscle itself (see page 77) may be a factor in coronary artery disease.

This is far from an exhaustive list of the ways in which smoking might affect coronary artery disease. Nor is it in the least unlikely that these or other mechanisms may combine to produce excess deaths from coronary artery disease. The important point here, as it has been made so often in previous chapters, is that the excess deaths really do occur, and that rational explanations are plentiful. The burden of proof is by now on those who seek to discredit the death rate statistics.

Until quite recently, it was possible to argue that smoking did not affect the occurrence of coronary artery disease at all, but merely increased the likelihood of a fatal outcome among men who already had partially blocked coronary arteries. A recent study by Drs. Joseph T. Doyle and Thomas R. Dawber makes this view no longer tenable — at least with respect to the type of heart disease called myocardial infarction. The Doyle-Dawber study covered 1,838 male civil servants aged 39-55 in the Albany, New York, area, and 2,282 male residents of Framingham, Mass., aged 30-62. All of these men were thoroughly examined for coronary artery disease at the beginning of the studies and were found to be free of it. They were then periodically re-examined over the next six to eight years. The conclusion: "Heavy cigarette smokers experience a three-fold increase in the *incidence* of myocardial infarction . . . as compared with non-smokers."

There is considerable evidence that it is the nicotine in the cigarettes which is primarily responsible for the effects of smoking on the cardiovascular system. And the evidence is very good that the amount of nicotine absorbed by the body is dependent largely on whether or not the smoker inhales. These findings, in turn, offer a reasonable explanation of why coronary artery disease is more common among heavy cigarette smokers, most of whom inhale, than among pipe and cigar smokers, few of whom inhale.

■ CANCER AT SITES NOT DIRECTLY EXPOSED TO SMOKE. One finding of the prospective studies which seems startling at first glance is the relationship between cigarette smoking and cancer of the liver, cancer of the bladder, and cancer at other sites not directly exposed to the smoke. Some 286 excess deaths from these forms of cancer were recorded among smokers in the Hammond-Horn study, as compared with 360 excess deaths from cancer of the lung. On closer examination, however, these relationships seem quite logical.

Cancer of the bladder is an example. Several studies have shown that industrial workers exposed to carcinogens are quite likely to develop cancer of the bladder despite the fact that the bladder is not initially exposed to the carcinogens. A reasonable assumption is that the carcinogens, and perhaps the co-carcinogens as well, enter the body and are excreted in concentrated form by the kidneys into the bladder. The bladder cells may be especially susceptible to them, or perhaps exposed to them over a more prolonged period than other body cells. This may or may not ultimately prove to be the explanation of increased cancer of the bladder among heavy cigarette smokers; it is at least sufficient to indicate, once again, that the relationship is not so remote or implausible as to challenge belief.

■ PULMONARY DISEASES such as influenza and bronchitis are closely related to smoking. The changes in the lungs of heavy cigarette smokers described in Chapter 5 give grounds for believing (1) that heavy cigarette smokers may be more likely to develop such diseases than non-smokers, and (2) that after such diseases are contracted heavy cigarette smokers may be more likely to die.

Emphysema. This disease of the lungs deserves special consideration for a number of reasons. First, it appears to have taken a sudden spurt, much as lung cancer did a generation ago. In California, for example, the emphysema death rate rose from 1.5 per 100,000 in 1950 to 9.5 in 1960, a six-fold increase. Further, the increase is noted primarily among men. And while less than one death in 200 is attributed to emphysema in recent (1958) national death statistics, the prevalence of the disease among the living is very high. Some estimates place the number of Americans suffering from emphysema at 10,000,000 or more. Many are disabled by the disease. The Social Security Administration pays more disability allowances to workers aged 50 through 64 for emphysema than for any other disease except heart disease.

No one knows what causes emphysema, but there is almost unanimous agreement among lung specialists that smoking makes it worse. At the same time, there is substantial evidence that air pollution is also a factor in the appearance or at least in the outcome of emphysema. This is another of the areas where research is needed.

A study published early in 1963 by Dr. Lemon and his associates at Loma Linda University School of Medicine in Los Angeles suggests, however, that smoking rather than air pollution is the major factor. The Lemon group checked deaths from emphysema, and deaths with emphysema as a contributing cause, among California Seventh Day Adventists and non-Adventists. The Adventists were distributed through the state in a way which suggested that they had received slightly less than (but close to) the same exposure to air pollution as other Californians. They might thus be expected, on the air pollution theory, to have about the same proportion of emphysema deaths as other Californians. Calculations showed that 22 deaths among them would be expected. Yet only four deaths attributed to emphysema were recorded.

Very few Seventh Day Adventists, as noted earlier, smoke cigarettes. Three of the four emphysema deaths among Seventh Day Adventists were among men with a long history of cigarette smoking; the smoking habits of the fourth could not be ascertained.

If Seventh Day Adventists were not in some way protected from emphysema, 51 deaths *with emphysema as a contributing cause* would have been expected among the Seventh Day Adventists in the Lemon study. In fact, only 14 such deaths were recorded, mostly among men with long histories of cigarette smoking.

■ CEREBRAL VASCULAR LESIONS (STROKES). A stroke generally results from the blocking of an artery in the brain by a blood clot (thrombus), or occasionally by the bursting of a brain artery. Patients with atherosclerosis are especially likely to have strokes. As noted above with respect to coronary artery disease, cigarette smoking *may* affect the fats or fatty acids in the blood and thus lead to atherosclerosis; or it may affect blood clotting and thus lead to thrombosis. It may also affect the bursting of small arteries. The association between cigarette smoking and strokes might be explained in any or all of these ways; but no one is really sure that these are true explanations. The most that can be said with confidence is that smokers appear to run a slightly greater risk than non-smokers of dying of strokes.

■ GASTRIC AND DUODENAL ULCERS. No one is sure that smoking increases the likelihood of ulcers; all that is known is that the likelihood of dying from them is greater in smokers — and that if patients with active ulcers continue to smoke, their recovery chances are reduced.

■ CANCER AT SITES DIRECTLY EXPOSED TO THE SMOKE. Here the evidence for a direct relationship is very good. The smoke contains carcinogens and co-carcinogens, and the lips, tongue, mouth, larynx, pharynx, and esophagus are directly exposed to these substances. Further, smoking produces local irritation which itself predisposes to cancer at the irritated sites. Presumably inhaling is not an important factor here; smokers who merely draw the smoke into their mouths, hold it there, and blow it out again may get as heavy a dose as inhalers — or conceivably a somewhat heavier dose. Pipe and cigar smokers who don't inhale the smoke may therefore be running substantially the same risk of cancer at these sites as cigarette smokers. The evidence on this point is not decisive.

On the other hand, cancer at these sites is much less common than lung cancer, even among heavy smokers; and these cancers are much more likely to be noticed and diagnosed early, treated in time, and thus cured. Pipe and cigar smokers can console themselves with these reassuring considerations — provided they consult a physician early if symptoms appear, or have their mouths and throats examined periodically even in the absence of symptoms.

■ BUERGER'S DISEASE is a relatively rare disease, limited almost entirely to smokers. The circulation of the blood through the extremities is impaired. In patients who continue to smoke, this impairment leads to gangrene, amputation, and ultimately death. Patients who stop smoking, in contrast, can be assured that the progression of the disease will almost certainly be halted. It is a startling fact indeed that some patients who have already lost their toes, and who have been warned that they will lose their legs next, nevertheless have continued to smoke.

Tobacco angina is another rare condition in which the relationship to smoking is direct and undoubted. Patients with this condition suffer heart pain, electrocardiographic changes, and other specific signs and symptoms of angina pectoris whenever they smoke a cigarette. Such patients, obviously, should stop smoking. However, this direct relationship to smoking is not apparent in the great majority of angina pectoris patients.

■ CIRRHOSIS OF THE LIVER. This disease, as noted earlier (page 28) seems to be caused by heavy drinking and the nutritional deficiencies often associated with heavy drinking. It thus seems likely that the apparent relationship between smoking and cirrhosis is actually an X-factor effect, showing up in the statistics merely because many heavy drinkers are also heavy smokers.

So-called X-factors capable of explaining in this way the relationship between smoking and *other* diseases are conspicuous by their absence.

In sum, death from coronary artery disease and death from lung cancer are the two major risks a cigarette smoker runs; these two diseases account for two thirds of the excess deaths among cigarette smokers. Some other diseases may not be directly associated with smoking, but non-smokers may have a better chance of recovery from them. For still others, smoking is in all probability a cause or contributing factor, but these diseases are rare even among smokers. There is no convincing evidence that the victims of *any* disease at all are helped by smoking.

SMOKING AND PHYSICAL COMPLAINTS. In addition to the greater risk of dying from certain diseases and the greater risk of contracting certain others, recent studies suggest that there is a lessened well-being among smokers according to their own accounts. The most impressive evidence for this comes from the preliminary reports of Dr. Hammond's gigantic study of more than a million men and women for the American Cancer Society.

The men and women enrolling in the study were asked not only about their smoking habits but also about their "current physical complaints," such as cough, sore throat, hoarseness, shortness of breath, pain or discomfort in the chest, difficulty in swallowing, constipation, diarrhea, stomach-ache, loss of appetite, headache, dizziness, insomnia, and so on. Further, they were asked to classify their complaints as "slight," "moderate," or "severe," or in some cases as occurring "seldom," "fairly often," or "often." The preliminary report covers such reports from 18,697 men and 24,371 women over 30, selected from the total responses.

Coughing, as might be expected, turned out to be the complaint most closely related to smoking. The relationship was far higher with cigarette smoking than with cigar or pipe smoking; and the larger the number of cigarettes smoked daily, the greater the proportion of respondents complaining of cough.

Shortness of breath and loss of appetite were also associated with smoking, to a somewhat lesser degree; and there were minor associations with other physical complaints.

Of special interest was the finding that heavy cigarette smokers reported more "nervous tension" than non-smokers. This seems to suggest that if smokers light cigarettes in order to curb nervous tension, they are not having much success. One possible interpretation of the evidence, of course, is that nervous tension leads to heavy cigarette smoking. An alternative interpretation is that smoking heightens nervous tension. And, of course, both may be true simultaneously.

No symptoms were found to be significantly rarer among smokers than among non-smokers.

CHAPTER 7
Ways to Cut the Risk

THE EVIDENCE we have reviewed is surely sufficient to persuade rational men and women that they would be better off not smoking — that they would, on the average, both live longer and stay healthier while they lived. But for many individuals, stopping smoking is not easy. The case of the late Dr. Sigmund Freud, founder of psychoanalysis and a confirmed cigar smoker, is a classic example.

Freud suffered an attack of influenza in 1894, at the age of 38, which left him with an irregular disturbance of his heartbeat (arrhythmia). His best friend and closest associate at the time, Dr. Wilhelm Fleiss, informed Freud that this was due to smoking, and ordered him to stop. Freud tried to stop, or cut down his ration, but failed. "He was always a heavy smoker — 20 cigars a day were his usual allowance," says Dr. Ernest Jones, himself a psychoanalyst, in his classic three-volume "Life and Work of Sigmund Freud." "In the course of the correspondence [between Fleiss and Freud] there are many references to this attempt to diminish or even abolish the habit, mainly on Fleiss's advice. But it was one respect in which even Fleiss's influence was ineffective."

Freud did stop for a time, it is true, but his subsequent depression and other symptoms — possibly psychosomatic, at least in part — proved unbearable. Freud himself described them in these terms:

"Soon after giving up smoking, there were tolerable days. . . .
Then there came suddenly a severe affection of the heart,
worse than I ever had when smoking. The maddest racing and
irregularity, constant cardiac tension, oppression, burning, hot
pain down the left arm, some dyspneia [labored breathing] of
a suspiciously organic degree — all that in two or three attacks
a day and continuing. And with it an oppression of mood in
which images of dying and farewell scenes replaced the more
usual fantasies. . . . The organic disturbances have lessened in
the last couple of days; the hypomanic mood continues. . . .It
is annoying for a doctor who has to be concerned all day long
with neurosis not to know whether he is suffering from a
justifiable or a hypochondriacal depression." Within seven
weeks, Freud was smoking heavily again.

Fleiss persisted in ordering Freud to give up cigars, however, and a little later Freud wrote that he was cutting down
to one cigar a week. After a few weeks, Dr. Jones reports,
Freud noted that the weekly cigar was losing its taste and
hoped to stop altogether.

He did stop — for 14 very long months. Apparently he suffered throughout this period. "Then he resumed," Dr. Jones
writes, "the torture being beyond human power to bear."

On another occasion, Freud decided to stop again, since his
pulse was very bad, and he found he couldn't cut down on
the number of cigars he smoked. Instead of smoking four
cigars a day and then struggling against a fifth, he decided,
it was "better to have the fight out with the first." Within a
month, he was smoking again.

More than 15 years later, at the age of 55, Freud was still
smoking 20 cigars a day — and still struggling against the
habit. In a letter to Dr. Jones he noted "the sudden intolerance
of [my] heart for tobacco."

Four years later he wrote to Dr. Karl Abraham that his passion for smoking hindered his psychological studies. But he kept on smoking.

In February 1923, at the age of 67, Freud noted sores on his right palate and jaw which failed to heal. It was cancer. An operation was performed, the first of 33 operations for cancer he endured during the 16 remaining years of his life. "I am still out of work and cannot swallow," he wrote shortly after this first operation. "Smoking is accused as the etiology of this tissue rebellion." Yet he continued to smoke.

The initial cancer was apparently cured, for it did not recur. Freud was free of cancer for eight years. But other places in his mouth began to go through the familiar series of precancerous stages. First, white patches called *leukoplakias* appeared; then, small growths called *papillomas* – a form of hyperplasia; and, finally, true invasive carcinoma. No doubt Freud himself followed with interest this step-by-step development of each new lesion in his mouth. His daughter Anna examined his mouth for him from time to time. He was repeatedly warned by eminent specialists whose judgment he trusted that smoking was the cause. He kept on smoking.

Occasionally, it is true, Freud tried very hard to stop and thought he had succeeded. One such occasion occurred in 1926, when he was 70. "It is pretty certain," he wrote, "that I show signs of a myocardial affection which cannot be dealt with simply by abstaining from smoking.... The number of my various bodily troubles make me wonder how long I shall be able to continue my professional work, especially since renouncing the sweet habit of smoking has resulted in a great diminution of my intellectual interests." Soon he was smoking again.

By now, Freud was having recognizable attacks of "tobacco angina" whenever he smoked. He tried partially denicotinized cigars, but even these produced cardiac discomfort. Nevertheless, he went on smoking.

At 73, Freud was ordered to retire to a sanitarium for a heart condition. He made an immediate recovery — "not through any therapeutic miracle," he wrote, "but through an act of autonomy." This act of autonomy, of course, was another firm decision to stop smoking. And Freud did stop — for 23 days. Then he started smoking a cigar a day. Then two. Then three or four. . . .

In 1936, at the age of 79, and in the midst of his endless series of mouth and jaw operations for cancer, Freud had more heart trouble. "It was evidently exacerbated by nicotine," Dr. Jones notes, "since it was relieved as soon as he stopped smoking." His jaw had been entirely removed and an artificial jaw substituted; he was almost constantly in pain; often he could not speak and sometimes he could not eat or swallow. Yet at the age of 80, Freud was still smoking what Dr. Jones calls "an endless series of cigars." He died of cancer in 1939, at the age of 83, after many years of intense suffering and tragic handicap. One can only speculate what his history would have been had he started his smoking career with cigarettes.

Was Freud "addicted" to smoking? The word "addiction," like the word "cause," can be so strictly defined that it loses any possible application, or it can be defined so as to apply solely to cocaine, morphine, and a few other narcotics. Dr. Jones himself has this to say of Freud's smoking: "That it might be called rather an addiction than a habit was shown by the extent to which he suffered when he was deprived of the opportunity to smoke." In any ordinary sense of the word, surely, Freud was a tobacco addict. And so are other smokers who find that, in spite of valiant efforts, they cannot stop.

Many smokers, however, including chain cigarette smokers

who have consumed two packs or more a day for many years, *are* able to stop when they decide the time has come. In retrospect at least, it seems to some of these ex-smokers that "breaking the habit" was easy, or was difficult for only a few days or weeks. This and other lines of evidence suggest that smoking may resemble the drinking of alcoholic beverages in this respect, affecting different people quite differently. Just as there are social drinkers, so there may be social smokers, who can stop without feeling deprived. But addicted smokers — "tobaccics" — may, like alcoholics, be so firmly "hooked" that stopping is extremely difficult or even impossible. More than will power appears to be involved. Far more research on this point, and on the specific substances in tobacco smoke, if any, which produce addiction in some smokers, is urgently needed. One study suggests that it is the nicotine itself which is addictive, and that hypodermic injections of nicotine will assuage the pangs of a smoker deprived of tobacco — but this has not been confirmed.

In addition to the smokers like Freud, so firmly addicted that they cannot stop smoking, and to those who could stop but only at a high price in discomfort or even suffering, there are no doubt many smokers who could stop without much trouble, but who enjoy the habit so that they would like to continue if it could be made reasonably safe. For the benefit of all these smokers, let us review next various approaches to the problem of lessening the dangers.

SAFER CIGARETTES. The ideal solution here, perhaps, would be the manufacture of a safe — or at least a substantially safer — cigarette; and studies seeking such a solution are no doubt under way behind the closed doors of the cigarette company research laboratories. The goal of a safer cigarette can be approached in a number of ways.

FILTER TIPS. It is commonly believed that a good filter tip on a cigarette will reduce the amount of nicotine in the smoke, and this is true. It is also commonly believed that a good filter tip will reduce the amount of a group of substances commonly called "tars" found in the smoke. This is true only in a Pickwickian sense, for the "tars" *are* condensed smoke; the only other substances you get from the cigarette are gases and other volatile components. Thus, reducing the nicotine and tars in the smoke is very nearly equivalent to reducing the smoke itself. Smoke without tars is almost like water with the liquid removed. For convenience, however, let us continue to use the common terms and say that a good cigarette filter should reduce both the nicotine content of the smoke and the tars in the smoke.

It is desirable to reduce the nicotine because, as we have seen, this substance is the chief suspect in the association between smoking and cardiovascular diseases. It is desirable to reduce the tars — that is, the smoke itself — because substances included in the tars are the chief suspects with respect to lung cancer, cancer at other sites directly exposed to the smoke, the lung changes described by the Auerbach team, and possibly other conditions.

A good filter can accomplish both of these purposes. But note the following three important limitations from which filters suffer.

First, not all filter-tip cigarettes really fulfill their purpose. Some pass almost as much nicotine and tar as some unfiltered cigarettes, and thus give smokers who select them for health reasons a false sense of security. If you decide to switch to a filtered cigarette for health reasons, try to select a brand which really will reduce your intake of both nicotine and tar per puff of smoke. This is difficult under present conditions because cigarettes are not labeled (as they should be) with the nicotine and tar content of their smoke. For a further discussion of labeling, see page 184.

Second, at least some smokers report a tendency to increase the number of cigarettes smoked when they switch from plain to filter cigarettes; or they smoke to a shorter butt. Thus they lose whatever advantage they might gain from smoking filter-tip cigarettes. Their intake of nicotine and tars may in some cases actually increase.

Third, switching to a filter-tip cigarette is not likely to solve the problem of patients with Buerger's disease, emphysema, tobacco angina, gastric or duodenal ulcer, or other conditions exacerbated by smoking. Even though the nicotine and tar levels are reduced, they may still be too high for safety in these conditions.

NON-INHALABLE CIGARETTES. A substantial body of evidence indicates that most of the damage done by smoking (with the possible exception of cancer of the lips, mouth, tongue, larynx, pharynx, and esophagus) is associated directly with inhaling rather than merely drawing the smoke into the mouth and blowing it out again. Modern cigarettes are designed to be inhaled; indeed, the "mildness" so strongly touted in the cigarette advertisements seems to be largely an inhalability factor. Pipe and cigar smoke are not mild in this sense. They are therefore rarely inhaled. One promising way to produce a safer cigarette, accordingly, might be to add something to the tobacco which would discourage inhaling, or to process the tobacco in such a way as to make inhaling very unpleasant.

Do not stand on one foot, however, while you wait for the major cigarette companies to start promoting non-inhalable cigarettes. For there is considerable reason to believe that such a cigarette would prove unpopular. Indeed, there are several "little cigars" now on the market which are the size and shape of cigarettes, but made of cigar-type tobacco. None of them is a best-seller. If you want a short smoke which *may* discourage inhaling, you might try these cigarette-sized cigars. But for a discussion of them, and a report on tests of them, see Appendix B, page 215.

"COOLER" SMOKE. One difference between cigar and pipe smoke on the one hand and cigarette smoke on the other is that the cigarette smoke is generated in a hotter combustion than the other two. This has led to the theory that cigarettes are more harmful because the hotter combustion gives rise to more harmful substances in the smoke. Efforts have therefore been made to achieve a safer cigarette by lowering the temperature of combustion.

This can be done quite simply by punching holes in the side of the cigarette, near the butt end, or by introducing a porous paper section in the wrapper. In either case, some air is drawn in through the side of the cigarette so that the draft on the ember when you take a drag is lessened and the temperature of combustion is thus perhaps lowered. You can achieve the same result without holes or porous sections in the cigarette, of course, by taking slow, gentle "sips" at the smoke instead of vigorous drags. The difficulty with both the "leaky" cigarette and the slow-sip approach is the notable paucity of evidence to prove that lowering the temperature of combustion really makes the smoke safer.

The lower temperature of combustion which may be achievable in these ways should not be confused with the widely advertised "coooooler" smoke due to menthol or other additives. There is no evidence in the scientific literature that merely mentholating a cigarette lowers the temperature of combustion.

"SELECTIVE" FILTERS. Conventional filters cut both the nicotine and the tar; but they do not selectively remove substances in the smoke known or suspected of being harmful — such as the carcinogens and co-carcinogens. Selective filters, in contrast, are designed to remove specific substances. At least two filters recently marketed claim to be selective, but their claims have not as yet been objectively evaluated.

A filter capable of removing such carcinogens as the polycyclic aromatic hydrocarbons (see page 45) from the smoke — or a cigarette additive capable of discouraging the formation of these hydrocarbons during tobacco combustion — might be a noteworthy development indeed; but no one has as yet claimed to have such a process.

One major problem researchers in these areas face is the difficulty of proving that such a cigarette really is safer after it has been developed. Suppose, for example, that a cigarette could be manufactured with smoke wholly free of phenols, "volatile irritants," polycyclic aromatic hydrocarbons, and other presumably harmful ingredients. Short of waiting a quarter of a century or more to see what happens to men and women who smoke them, it would be hard to devise a conclusive safety test. It is also conceivable that the substances in the smoke which do the harm are the very substances which lead to smoker satisfaction or to smoker addiction.

CHANGES IN PATTERN OF SMOKING. Taking fewer puffs on a cigarette is one obvious way of reducing your intake of both nicotine and tar — provided you don't throw away the advantage by lighting more cigarettes.

Another possibility is to take the same number of drags on the cigarette, but to take them all during a short period of time immediately after you have lit up. There is excellent evidence that the first drags on a cigarette are the safest because the smoke is drawn through the long stem and filtered on its way to your mouth and lungs. Some of the nicotine and tar are trapped as they are drawn through the tobacco. The tobacco thus fills up with nicotine and tar, and these substances are burned a second time as the ember approaches the butt. Thus, as the butt-end of the cigarette is smoked, the proportion of nicotine and tar per puff goes up and up. (As a reminder of this, companies might put a red line, like the Plimsoll's mark on ships, around their cigarettes an inch or so from the butt-end.) One study at the Roswell Park Memorial Institute in Buffalo, New York, suggests that the tenth drag on a cigarette contains 2.5 times as much tar as the first. If you insist on taking ten or more drags on a cigarette, the Roswell Park researchers suggest, take them in rapid succession while the butt is still long. But such a maneuver is likely to have only a minor effect on your total intake. And there is always the possibility that the number of cigarettes you smoke will increase if you try to cut down on nicotine and tars through such tactics.

SWITCHING TO PIPES OR CIGARS. For confirmed cigarette smokers who find they cannot stop smoking altogether, this may prove the best solution. It is the solution adopted by Dr. E. Cuyler Hammond after completing his prospective study of what happens to cigarette, pipe, and cigar smokers.

An important qualification should be noted, however, to the general position that pipes and cigars are safer than cigarettes. The vast majority of pipe and cigar smokers do not inhale, and it is the experience of these non-inhalers which weighs the evidence in favor of pipes and cigars. Conceivably a man who inhales cigarette smoke for a quarter-century and then switches to cigars or a pipe may learn to inhale their smoke as well. If he does, there is no reason to believe that his life expectancy will improve or that his risk of lung cancer or other diseases will be lowered. On the contrary, he may be even worse off than when he inhaled cigarette smoke.

Heavy cigar and pipe smokers should also note that they may

run more or less the same risk as heavy cigarette smokers with respect to cancer of the lips, tongue, mouth, and perhaps throat. They should therefore have a mouth-and-throat examination periodically, and should consult a physician if sores fail to heal promptly or if other symptoms appear.

A curious phenomenon of our modern society is the failure of the pipe manufacturers, the pipe tobacco distributors, and the cigar makers to publicize the substantial margin of safety their products enjoy over cigarettes. Toothpaste makers spend vast sums in publicizing a comparatively minor advantage of one brand or another with respect to tooth decay. Tobacco companies in the past have not hesitated to exploit to the hilt far smaller and more dubious advantages. Since the cigar and pipe people are hiding their virtues under a bushel, it's up to the rest of us to make the facts better known.

In particular, we should make them known to boys just starting out on their smoking careers. The best advice to give a boy, of course, is not to smoke at all. But if he is going to smoke anyway, the lesser risk from a pipe or cigars should surely be called to his attention. This advantage may be particularly important at the *beginning* of a boy's smoking career, when he is forming the habit of inhaling or not inhaling.

Whether girls, too, might be encouraged to smoke pipes or cigars instead of cigarettes is a complicated question. Women's pipes are available, and make their appearance from time to time on college campuses. The pipe-smoking "granny" is also a recognizable American folk character. Cigar smoking among American women has apparently been limited to a few eccentrics such as the late Amy Lowell; but in some other countries women cigar smokers are less rare. Until recently, American girls started smoking cigarettes at an older age than boys. They smoked fewer cigarettes on the average; and more girls were total abstainers or smoked only on rare social occasions. Recent reports from some communities, however, suggest that girls are now starting as early as boys and smoking as much or more. If this trend becomes general, the encouragement of pipe and cigar smoking among girls may change from an amusing possibility to an urgently needed public health measure. The least that can be said is that where girls are permitted to smoke cigarettes, they should not be forbidden to smoke pipes or cigars if they so choose.

SMOKING FEWER CIGARETTES. This no doubt lowers the risk — if you don't compensate by taking more puffs on each cigarette you light, or by smoking the cigarette to a shorter butt. Some confirmed cigarette smokers report, moreover, that of all the possible approaches, cutting down on cigarettes is the hardest to carry out day after day after day. Freud himself, it will be recalled, thought (at least occasionally) that it was easier to stop than to cut down.

STOPPING SMOKING ALTOGETHER. This is by far the soundest alternative for the smoker, just as the safest alternative for any non-smoker is to continue not to smoke.

One question occasionally asked is whether a generation of non-smokers might not pick up some alternative habit or addiction which might prove even more damaging than smoking in the long run. This is no doubt a possibility. There is no evidence to date, however, that ex-smokers become habituated to anything else. When the estimate is recalled that a million children now in school will die of lung cancer by the age of 70 if present trends continue — not to mention the evidence linking smoking to coronary artery disease and other fatal or disabling conditions — the evils we know not of are likely to appear quite modest in comparison with the evils we can be very sure will follow if we remain a cigarette-addicted society.

PART II

The Industry:
Science & Public Relations

CHAPTER 8
What Should an Industry Do?

"THE ECONOMIC HEALTH of the industry is being jeopardized by an unrelenting negative force — a force for which it cannot compensate." So ran a comment in *Printer's Ink*, an advertising trade journal, not long ago.

"Fate has conspired to make this particular moment a testing time for tobacco. The industry is being ganged by many problems." So said Spencer B. Hanes, executive vice president of the R. J. Reynolds Tobacco Company, at the end of 1962, looking ahead to 1963.

What should an industry do when its products are charged with causing or being accomplices to many thousands of deaths a year? How should it have been conducting itself during the past ten years while the unrelenting evidence of the health hazard of cigarettes has been conspiring to jeopardize the industry's health? There would seem to have been four courses of action the cigarette companies might have followed, and it may be useful to review them briefly here.

It is an obviously Utopian conceit that the cigarette companies, at the first reports of the smoking-health link, might have taken the public-spirited position that cigarettes were guilty until proved innocent and discontinued their manufacture. And it is doubtful that the general public would have accepted such a position had the companies taken it.

It is conceivable that the companies might have elected to ignore the health charges altogether. To be sure, this decision would have been a clean-cut one; but it would have been high-handed, 19th-century-capitalist style behavior outdated in a business world dominated by public relations psychology with its notion that business, if it cannot be devoted to the public good, at least ought to look as though it were.

The other choices were the feasible ones. The first of these would have been to say that, while the cigarette-health link hadn't been established to the industry's satisfaction, it hadn't been disproved, either, so a strong burden of proof was on the industry itself. The cigarette companies might have urged caution on smokers; they could have given significant amounts of money to independent research organizations; they could have avoided propaganda and controversy in favor of clarification and unbiased inquiry.

The fourth choice for the industry was to consider those who opposed it as adversaries, to act like lords of a beleagured feudal castle, while using the techniques of modern public relations to reassure the smoking public. It was to attempt to turn a serious question of public health into a controversy — in short, to fight. It was this choice that the industry made.

"Perhaps the time has arrived for the tobacco industry to take off the gloves and fight back with the political and economic weaponry that a gigantic industry can muster," the trade publication *Tobacco* said early in 1963, echoing what must have been general cigarette business sentiments in 1953, when the "health scare," as the industry still calls it, may be said to have started seriously. The cigarette industry is not gigantic, but it is big business. In 1962 some 63,000,000 people — about 37,500,000 men and 25,500,000 women, or roughly half the adult population of the U.S. — smoked cigarettes, averaging about a pack a day and paying nearly $7 billion for the privilege. There are six major manufacturers of cigarettes and, among them, they account for over 99 per cent of the sales. These companies have been virtually united on their approach to the health charges. Five of the six, along with tobacco warehouse and growers' associations, banded together in 1953 to form the Tobacco Industry Research Committee (the T.I.R.C.), ever since then the industry's voice.

The cigarette industry's original comment on the health question was signalled in 448 newspapers on January 4, 1954, in full-page newspaper ads entitled "A Frank Statement to Cigarette Smokers" and sponsored by the T.I.R.C. "Recent reports on experiments with mice," the ad said, "have given wide publicity to a theory that cigarette smoking is in some way linked with lung cancer in human beings . . . we feel it is in the public interest to call attention to the fact that eminent doctors and research scientists have questioned the claimed significance of these experiments."

The ad pledged aid in tobacco-health research, to be supervised by a scientist of "unimpeachable integrity and national repute" and an advisory board of "distinguished scientists disinterested in the cigarette industry." The aim, said the then-president of the American Tobacco Company, Paul M. Hahn, was to "Let the results speak for themselves, whatever they are."

But in a subsequent press release the T.I.R.C. made it plain that the facts would not have to speak entirely for themselves. For one of the objects of the T.I.R.C. would be "to make available to the public factual information on this subject." To aid in doing so, the T.I.R.C. hired the well-known public relations firm of Hill & Knowlton, Inc., which had and has such clients as the aerospace, pharmaceutical, and iron and steel industries, and is a specialist in industry association groups.

The T.I.R.C., then, is a marriage of research and public relations, and the difficulties the organization faces in the latter arena have been well-stated by *P. R. Reporter*, a trade journal: "Hit repeatedly ... with well-publicized charges that cigarette smoking may contribute to lung cancer and heart disease, the U.S. tobacco industry today faces a public relations problem of a magnitude and complexity perhaps unequalled in modern industrial history. ... What gives it complexity is the fact that the industry is on the defensive against charges that could prove true, in which case its position would become retroactively indefensible. The fact that the industry itself is spending millions of dollars ... in researching causes of lung and heart ailments and could come up tomorrow with conclusive evidence of its own that would hang it does not make the problem any simpler." The tobacco industry, the publication said, has "a cause without a case."

The case the T.I.R.C. has lacked is the ability to disprove the health charges or even to come up with a defense acceptable to a significant part of the scientific community. Under these circumstances, the T.I.R.C.'s response has been somewhat monotonous. The T.I.R.C., and, by extension, the tobacco industry, has had two principal spokesmen: Timothy V. Hartnett, chairman of the Committee and the retired president of the Brown & Williamson Tobacco Corp.; and Dr. Clarence Cook Little, the T.I.R.C.'s scientific director. Whenever a new finding implicating cigarettes has been announced, Mr. Hartnett or Dr. Little has come forth to deny that it is true or new or meaningful.

DENIALS AND REBUTTALS. The 1954 report of the Cancer Society, the famous Hammond-Horn report discussed in Part I, "points up the need for further research," the T.I.R.C. said. On a resolution adopted by Buffalo, N.Y., health officials, Dr. Little commented, "No convincing clinical or experimental evidence has yet been brought forward that cigarette smoking is the positive cause of lung cancer," to which Mr. Hartnett added that "medical and scientific opinion remains widely divided over the significance of various statistical relationships between smoking and cancer or any other ailments." As for the Auerbach analysis of lung tissue, showing that precancerous lung conditions occur in a high relationship to heavy smoking, Mr. Hartnett said, " . . . it would be presumptuous of us to discuss his findings." "The time for positive statements has not yet arrived," Dr. Little remarked, and Mr. Hartnett, in a speech to tobacco men, said strongly, "Let's get a couple of things straight. Nobody has produced evidence proving that cigarette smoking causes lung cancer."

A survey of doctors' opinions on the dangers of smoking published in 1955 was, Mr. Hartnett felt, "biased, non-scientific, and filled with shortcomings and defects;" and, speaking again about the Hammond-Horn study, he commented sadly, "It would be tragic if an overpublicized allegation that lacks scientific support were to divert and impede public or private support of sound research in such an important field of health." "Much more information is needed," the T.I.R.C. said in 1956, adding, "Everyone has a right to a personal opinion and one must expect that certain individuals will continue to hold definite and fixed views against the use of tobacco." A medical study group report "represents the viewpoints of seven individuals," Mr. Hartnett said, and a statement that a safer cigarette could be produced was based "on a number of assumptions that have not been established. . . ." The conclusions of the British Medical Research Council, Mr. Hartnett observed in 1957, "represent opinions about a theory of cause and effect not confirmed by scientific experiments and widely challenged in the world of science." As for the U.S. Surgeon General's 1958 statement on the subject, it "adds nothing new

..." Dr. Little said. A 1958 survey of 200,000 men by the U.S. Public Health Service contributed "no new information" and a statement by the Commissioner of the New York State Department of Health "skimmed off the most extreme positions of tobacco's most extreme critics . . . ," according to a statement by Mr. Hartnett.

By 1959, Mr. Hartnett was sure that "compelling doubts have been raised about statistics and their interpretations involving smoking and health." Taking aim, he said, "On the basis of past experience the anti-smoking campaign announced by the American Cancer Society may be expected to be a one-sided propaganda effort. . . . Through past centuries, there have been many such one-sided health attacks on tobacco, and they too were based on an anti-smoking bias rather than on fact." Mr. Hartnett was perhaps tiring, for, concerning a study by Dr. Dorn, he said, "We can see no reason to rehash these statistical figures. . . ." But in 1960 he reminded the National Tuberculosis Association, after its statement implicating cigarettes, "Surely some members of the NTA must remember that not too long ago there were charges that cigarette smoking caused tuberculosis. . . ." In 1963, after ten years of such denials and ten years of research supporting the smoking-health link, Dr. Little had changed not at all. "There have been and will continue to be speculations and opinions on the causes," he said, "but it is a matter of scientific fact that, in our present state of knowledge, no one knows the answers."

These rebuttals or denials have been presented at medical meetings and given to editors planning articles on the smoking-health link. In several instances news stories were substantially changed after the T.I.R.C. presented its material. Newspaper editors, not necessarily out of fear of offending advertisers but quite possibly because the issues *are* complex and the T.I.R.C. releases reassuring, have used the releases plentifully.

CRITICISMS AND CHARGES. For its public relations activities the T.I.R.C. has been criticized in many quarters. For example, the advertising journal, *Printers' Ink,* has called Mr. Hartnett a man of "few — but highly predictable — words: 'Nothing has been proved.' " The magazine went on to say, "The time has come, obviously, for the T.I.R.C. (and its equally ineffectual companion, the Tobacco Institute) to drop this injured, defensive tone and say and do something more positive. The industry's current problems won't just disappear . . . by disclaiming them."

Cameron Day, *Printers' Ink* managing editor, has explained why the publication chose to join the health fray. "Our job," he said, "is to be alert to problems that will affect advertisers. We think that as the evidence mounts there is more likelihood that cigarette advertising will face restraint by government regulation. We are not crusaders, but we don't like the idea of such restraints and certainly try to avoid them for cigarettes or anything else. The tobacco industry should be contributing more to solving the problem than it is. We don't think the T.I.R.C. has been very helpful."

Criticism of a different sort has come from those who believe the press has been rather too fair-minded with the tobacco industry. One of the sharpest of these critics was John Kenneth Galbraith, former Ambassador to India, Paul M. Warburg Professor of Economics at Harvard, and author of *The Affluent Society.* In a letter to *The New York Times,* he charged the *Times* with treating a research report and a Hartnett statement with equal respect. "Does not this seeming impartiality mean, in fact, that you are allowing Mr. Hartnett to use you for his purposes in a rather outrageous way?" Galbraith wrote.

"For years now the tobacco industry has been capping careful research reports with these unsupported denials. I certainly wouldn't want to suggest that you suppress Mr. Hartnett, but

111

shouldn't you remind your readers of these past denials and the predictable character of this one? Indeed, shouldn't you make it wholly clear that you are not equating the work of a careful researcher extending over the years with the press release of an industry spokesman ... ?

"Once Americans had an inspired nose for such special interest and a gifted ear for special pleading. They also had a most rewarding reaction. Mr. Hartnett's contentions would have been met by raucous charges of special pleading. He would have been proclaimed the most suspect of all possible witnesses. . . .

"But now dimmed perceptions, or incapacity for indignation, or perhaps mere indifference, means there is no reaction of any kind."

To the American Cancer Society, the T.I.R.C. is fighting a "delaying action ... to mislead the public into believing that no change in smoking habits is indicated from the existing statistical and pathological evidence, nor will be until 'direct experimental evidence' is at hand."

To Dr. Michael Shimkin, former director of field studies, National Cancer Institute, U.S. Public Health Service, and now Professor of Medicine at Temple University, "It's perhaps the natural response of an industry faced with change or extinction — obfuscation close to actual lies. I'm surprised they haven't recognized the writing on the wall clearer than they have, but it may be the most clever legal defense they can muster. And it is legalistic, not scientific."

But it is not necessary to go out of the tobacco industry to find criticisms of the T.I.R.C. One company, Liggett & Myers, did not join the organization, and its vice-president in charge of research, Dr. Frederick R. Darkis, has indicated why. "As far as I can visualize," he said, "the T.I.R.C. has been mostly a publicity organization. They have given millions to various research analysts, but it is very difficult to know what purpose the money has served."

Whether or not it was so planned at the outset, the T.I.R.C.'s constant statements that the findings are not conclusive have kept the speculation alive, and there is little doubt that the steady smoker can find, in this conflict, the justification not to stop.

CHAPTER 9
Scientists, Public Relations, and Tobacco

SCIENCE FUNCTIONS for the Tobacco Industry Research Committee in the shape of its Scientific Advisory Board,
composed of eight independent scientists or medical men and
Dr. Little, who also represents the T.I.R.C. on the Board. There
is no reason to question the scientific integrity of these advisors,
none of whom receives more than a small per diem for his
services. It is the function of the advisors to determine the
T.I.R.C.'s grant program, for which the tobacco industry has
donated $6.25 million from 1954 to date, each company giving
according to its sales. The T.I.R.C. has so far used this money
for close to 400 grants to researchers in 90 institutions, plus a
number of summer research fellowships to medical students.
The terms of a T.I.R.C. grant seem perfectly straightforward
— a grantee works on his own and is free to publish the results
where he likes.

Some have criticized the T.I.R.C.-sponsored research as being too long-range to be of much real help with the immediate
problem; to these critics the T.I.R.C. ought to be mostly concerned with the direct removal of carcinogenic elements from
smoke. To others, though, the T.I.R.C. is faithfully researching in fruitful areas. Another criticism is that the T.I.R.C.'s
research effort is too modest — the $800,000 allotted for re-
search in 1963 is about one half of one per cent of the indus-

114

try's intended advertising outlay, and about half the amount spent for research by a far smaller West German cigarette industry. To these figures, however, must be added whatever costs there may be for the cigarette companies' private research efforts, which are being conducted in an atmosphere of secrecy that would do credit to the Central Intelligence Agency.

Where the scientific advisors themselves do seem vulnerable is in the support which they have given to the public relations side of the T.I.R.C.; they have certainly helped provide the "eminent scientist" backing for the T.I.R.C.'s publicity. The Scientific Advisory Board itself has made statements supporting the T.I.R.C. position and Dr. Little, in making his denials to the press, has been identified with the Scientific Advisory Board. It can thus be said that though the scientific advisors are presumably presiding over objective scientific research, they have taken sides, which lowers their claims to impartiality.

One would expect, certainly, to find the Scientific Advisory Board united on the health question, but this is evidently not the case. It is said, apocryphally or not, that a Board member, also doing work for the American Cancer Society, smoked in the afternoon but not in the morning. One Board member, Dr. Paul Kotin, in explaining where he stood on the health issue, quoted a paper written by himself and a co-worker, Dr. Hans L. Falk: "The statement . . . to the effect that 'The sum total of scientific evidence establishes beyond reasonable doubt that cigarette smoking is a causative factor in the rapidly increasing incidence of human epidermoid cancer of the lung' represents a more or less universally accepted viewpoint with which we concur."

Dr. Kotin is chief of the Carcinogenesis Studies Branch of the National Cancer Institute of the U.S. Public Health Service, and a well-known cancer researcher as well as a member of the Scientific Advisory Board. He is among a number of scientists who were once dubious about the cigarette-health link but who are now satisfied that cigarettes are at least partially guilty. "Obviously," he says, "I disagree with Dr. Little on that point." Dr. Kotin was asked why he had remained a member of the Board. "My idea," he said, "was that either the cigarette-health question had to be ignored, which obviously it couldn't be, or something had to be done. If industry can be made to foot the bill to reduce the health hazard, that would be good, I reasoned. My notion was to provide the leadership to make the industry face its responsibilities."

DR. LITTLE. The most difficult of jobs has fallen to Dr. Little, who is a distinguished biologist, former president of the Universities of Maine and Michigan, and former director of the Roscoe B. Jackson Memorial Laboratory at Bar Harbor, Maine. These credentials are impressive. Moreover, Dr. Little, from 1929 until 1945, was managing director of the American Society for the Control of Cancer, as the American Cancer Society was then called.

Dr. Little's activities are not confined to administering the T.I.R.C.'s research grants. He has also testified before Congress and served as a medical expert in a court case. He has written articles on the health issue and he has issued many public statements. Before Dr. Little had accepted it, the job of scientific director of the T.I.R.C. was also discussed with one of the research scientists of the American Cancer Society. He was not opposed to accepting the position on principle, but he did have certain reservations, the main one being that he would be asked only to supervise independent research and not be required to make public statements or participate in a public relations campaign. Dr. Little was evidently willing to take on both roles.

"Many of my friends had expected me to jump on the smoking-causes-cancer bandwagon and start blowing an instrument," Dr. Little once told a reporter. "As long as the cause of cancer is unknown, I do not rule out that smoking or anything else is involved. But I believe emphatically that it's a disservice to the public to say that if we eliminated smoking we would eliminate 90 per cent of lung cancer."

Dr. Little's view is that the causative role of cigarettes in disease has not been proved, and that tobacco's part in the genesis of disease has not been properly identified. Before a truly informed opinion can be given, more research is needed, Dr. Little has argued, and continues to argue despite the lengthening record of research reviewed in the first part of this book. He fears, he says, that present anti-cigarette research will be overthrown, with the unhappy effect of shaking public confidence in research and disrupting public education in cancer prevention.

"People find it hard to believe that the T.I.R.C. is made up of scientists completely uninfluenced by the tobacco industry," Dr. Little has said. His only criticism of the industry is that it puts too much money into filtered-cigarette research, in which he has little interest, and which he thinks would be better spent in purer types of research activity. Ultimately, Dr. Little's argument seems to come down to the questions of causation and the rights of the researcher. "The public," he has written, "has been heavily propagandized along one definite theory of causation by those convinced by one level of information. Some of us demand a different order and level of knowledge before we accept causation or condone presentation of conclusions to the public. We claim merely the right to pursue knowledge through scientific research, the right to hold our own point of view, and the right of the public to be aware of it."

Dr. Little has made, fairly recently, several statements in which he agreed that moderation was always wise policy in anything, including smoking. But he put it much more strongly in 1944, when he was managing director of what is now the American Cancer Society. "Although no definite evidence exists concerning the relation between the use of tobacco and the incidence of lung cancer," he wrote, "it would seem unwise to fill the lungs repeatedly with a suspension of fine particles of a tobacco product of which smoke consists. It is difficult to see how such particles can be prevented from becoming lodged in the walls of the lungs and when so located how they can avoid producing a certain amount of irritation. One might also question the ultimate results of continued inhalation of the type of atmosphere which characterizes the lower levels of city streets. Experimental work with animals involving these matters is still inconclusive but it seems probable that the lung as an organ is not immune to the effects of chronic irritation and that it will in this respect resemble other organs of the body. Such being the case, wisdom in avoiding unnecessary lung irritation seems to be established." No such caution, however, exists in the statements of the T.I.R.C., where even to hint that anything might be amiss with tobacco is evidently considered apostasy.

DR. HAMMOND. Dr. Little's counterpart in the scientific aspect of the controversy, Dr. E. Cuyler Hammond, is a 51-year-old biometrist, formerly a medical statistician with the Army Air Force; he did some of the first statistical analyses of what the atomic bomb did to populations. After the war, Dr. Hammond came to the American Cancer Society. "The first thing I did here was to look at the trends," he has said. "I observed that while the death rate from other diseases was going down, there was a sharp rise in the incidence of lung cancer. It stood out. Before the war, I had worked, at Johns Hopkins, with Dr. Raymond Pearl, who had found a statistical association between smoking and the total death rate, so I knew about the prob-

118

lem. Dr. Pearl, by the way, had made a study, in the 1920s, showing that fruit flies couldn't live without alcohol — he was a hero of the anti-prohibitionists! His 1930 studies, implicating cigarettes, weren't nearly so popular. For myself, I was convinced that some agent in the environment was responsible for the rise in the lung cancer death rate, but I put cigarettes at the bottom of the list."

Dr. Hammond remembers that an early difference existed between Dr. Little and himself, Dr. Hammond being doubtful that cigarettes were the causative agent, Dr. Little being much and Dr. Horn, a psychologist with a strong background in statistics, launched their mammoth prospective study (see page 34). Dr. Hammond chose cigarettes as a starting point partly because of the Pearl study and partly because cigarettes were an easier factor to isolate from the environment than, for instance, gasoline exhaust or particles from rubber tires, both of which were higher on the list of Dr. Hammond's suspects. Dr. Hammond, himself then a three-to-four-pack-a-day smoker, was sure that cigarettes would be cleared, but nonetheless he notified the cigarette companies about his study, thinking that they might want to get ready in case the findings proved positive. "They paid no attention to us," he has said.

Before the results of his study were half in, Dr. Hammond, staggered, realized which way they were heading. "The important thing was the rise in the total death rate for smokers against non-smokers," he says. "I don't think I myself would have stopped had it just been for lung cancer — the risk might have seemed too small, large as it was. But the total death rate statistics were truly frightening."

Dr. Little, of course, has disagreed with Dr. Hammond's use of the statistics, and Dr. Hammond has undertaken to explain why. "There is a real difference between observational and experimental studies," he has said. "Astronomy, for instance, is based on observational studies, and yet it has been the most accurate of sciences. In observational studies you try not to alter the environment — you merely attempt to see what is happening as accurately as you can. The weakness of the observational approach is that while you can find out that something is happening you often don't know why. In experimental studies, though, you *try* to alter the environment to observe the results. Typically, you do something to one group and not to the other. The investigator purposely changes something. In experimental studies you are better able to set your variables, but this is difficult when the subject is people.

"Both approaches, observational and experimental, are needed in science. Dr. Little represents the experimental camp. It's beyond dispute that he's correct in saying that we don't know the exact causal mechanism between smoking and disease, though we know more about even that than Dr. Little implies. But it doesn't mean that we don't know what is happening.

"A great deal of semantics has gone into this debate. Take a key word, 'statistics.' The tobacco people attack statistics as though it were a dirty word. What is statistics? It is nothing more than handling data from more than one individual observation. Even an experimentalist couldn't work without statistics. Comparing percentages is standard scientific technique.

"The other key word is cause. There's no such thing in the world as simple cause and effect involving only one factor. Causes are always multiple. What we say is that cigarettes are a principal factor in the causation of lung cancer and other diseases, not the only cause. But they are a highly important causative factor, and we say that on the basis of statistical, pathological, clinical, and experimental evidence which no amount of arguing will blow away."

Dr. Shimkin amplifies this view by saying, "If you ask for

120

proof of a causal mechanism between cigarettes and disease on a molecular level we haven't got it. We can't say exactly what the mechanisms are. But biology doesn't demand that sort of proof. In terms of the kind of proof biology does demand, we've got it."

Another interpretation of the controversy is offered by Francis Bello, a member of the board of editors of *Scientific American*, who has made a detailed study of the question of cigarettes and health. To Bello, "What's happening has some counterpart in such issues as the Church vs. Galileo on the question of whether the earth was the center of the solar system, except that here the stakes are economic rather than theological. It's forgotten now, but there was considerable evidence on both sides of such questions. In the earth-sun controversy, for instance, there was evidence that the earth was stationary. If you dropped something it didn't fall behind you, as might have been expected if the earth was moving. A key principle, inertia, wasn't understood. Similarly, there are things not yet understood about smoking and lung cancer. For example, it is obvious that not all heavy smokers get cancer. Presumably, this merely means that some people are tougher than others. But it seems to give the tobacco industry a lot of comfort. Hammond and the others may be wrong, but, if so, it will be one of the greatest scientific flukes of all time.

"Eventually, the findings will be accepted by everyone. Smoking will be considered a risk, like a lot of other things in life. People do for pleasure what they want to do. What has happened before in science will happen again."

CHAPTER 10
The Rise of the Cigarette

TOBACCO, like coffee, chocolate, and cane sugar, is one of the blessings conferred on civilization by the New World. Unlike them, tobacco is not a food and its rapid acceptance during the last 450 years is an occurrence not easily explained. It may be that tobacco, as a French philosopher once observed about suffering, creates its own places in the human soul, places that only it can fill. An early euphemism about it, "bound in aromatic chains," suggests what researchers have only begun to probe — that tobacco use is some kind of an addiction, as it certainly seems to have been to Freud (see page 91).

Smoking itself — that is, non-tobacco smoking — had been practiced in ancient Greece and elsewhere, but it was evidently considered medicine, not pleasure, and, in any case, the substances smoked, such as dried cow dung, never quite caught on. Tobacco was native only to the Americas, and its original users were the Indians, some of whom snuffed it through a Y-shaped pipe called a taboca, from which the word tobacco may be derived. The first Europeans to see tobacco were Christopher Columbus and his crew, and the Europeans, rapidly recovering from the shock of seeing the Indians "drinking smoke," took to the habit with alacrity, bringing it back with them. The explorers also brought tobacco seeds, and before long the plant was under cultivation in Europe and along global trading routes.

The genus of the plant is called *Nicotiana,* after Jean Nicot, the French ambassador to Portugal who introduced it to the French court, claiming that it had near-magical curative powers for, among other things, cancer. Another Frenchman, a monk named Thevet, wanted credit for having introduced the plant to the Old World; the subsequent controversy could have been avoided had it been realized that the two men were dealing with different species. Nicot's plant was what is now called *N. Rustica,* a harsh tobacco that is currently under cultivation only in parts of Soviet Russia and the Near East. Thevet's is now called *N. Tabacum,* which, milder and more aromatic, is what we use today.

It was probably inevitable that a product with no use, food value or tradition and whose one purpose was pleasure, should run afoul of the Establishment, and tobacco had its troubles almost from the beginning. In Russia, early tobacco users were threatened with having their noses slit for a first offense and with death for persistent violations. In the 17th century, James I of England issued a *Counterblaste to Tobacco* in which he declared that smoking is "A Custome lothsome to the eye, hatefull to the Lungs, and in the blacke stinking fume thereof, neerest resembling the horrible Stigian smoak of the pit that is bottomeless."

In addition to the royal objection to tobacco there was also a medical one, for doctors considered it an important part of the pharmacopeia and objected to its indiscriminate use. This medical position was put by one Dr. Venner, of Bathe, in 1650, who said, "I will summarily rehearse the hurts that tobacco infereth, if it be used contrary to the order and way I have set downe. It driethe the brain, dimmith the sight, vitiateth the smell, dulleth and dejecteth both the appetite and the stomach, destroyeth the decoction, disturbeth the humours and the spirits, corrupteth the breath, induceth a trembling of the limbs, exsiccathe the windpipe, lungs and liver, annoyeth the milt and scorcheth the heart. . . ."

Danger to the decoction and the milt does not seem to have dissuaded tobacco users any more than James' veiled suggestion that smokers would, or should, go to hell, and the pit that proved bottomeless was the need for tobacco. As the product grew more plentiful, the habit pervaded all classes of society and was soon recognized by the state as an important source of revenue. It proved capable of surviving onslaughts by the government, religion, and science, of overriding threats, propaganda, high prices, and poor quality. "It is remarkable," the British Royal College of Physicians observed in its famous report, *Smoking and Health* (see page 65), "that tobacco should have attained such wide popularity among people quite unaccustomed to it, particularly since the early tobaccos produced a rank smoke with a much higher nicotine content than modern smokers would relish."

Tobacco has thus proved exceedingly durable. It has also shown, like Proteus, a marvelous ability to change its form. "Different ways of enjoying tobacco (snuff, chewing, pipe, cigars, nargileh) in different countries, its incorporation in social usages and rituals, its varying accessibility to minors and women, the social approval or penalties it entails, the changing patterns of different periods — all bespeak its dependence on the prevailing culture," says *Smoking and Health*, and Dr. Hammond suggests that tobacco consumption *per consumer* (as opposed to per capita) may have varied less over the centuries than one would suppose.

The cigarette made its first European appearance in Spain, where it was considered a poor man's smoke; English soldiers saw the Turks using it during the Crimean war, brought it back home with them, and from there it spread to the continent and to America. Cigarettes were smoked here before the Civil War, but, at least partly because of high prices, they did not really become popular until after the turn of the century. A usual reason given for the subsequent rise of cigarettes is that during World War I millions of soldiers began smoking them. Cigarettes, so the theory goes, are a soldier's smoke, easy to ship and carry.

But if one considers the objections to other forms of tobacco use in a city it becomes clear that cigarettes were almost bound to prevail, with or without war or even advertising. In the United States, chewing was for long the most popular form of tobacco use — Dickens, in his pre-Civil War travels here, complained bitterly about American chewing and spitting — and it was not until 1921 that cigarettes overtook chewing tobacco, as well as pipes and cigars, in per capita consumption. Chewing tobacco requires a spittoon and a good aim, and the habit was certain to lapse in a society whose household gods were cleanliness and sanitation. Cigars and pipes, too, have disadvantages. They are messy. The cigar smoker chews his stub and the pipe smoker is always spilling ashes. Both have strong aromas and may offend others in close quarters. Pipes, especially, are always going out and require rapt attention. Both need time and leisure to use properly, and time is the city's shortest commodity.

The cigarette can be smoked in a few minutes. It is relatively inoffensive. Everybody can use it. Unlike previous forms of tobacco, the cigarette, especially the modern cigarette, is mild and getting milder and the smoke can be readily inhaled into the lungs. And at approximately the right time — that is, about as long after cigarettes came to be mass consumed as it takes lung cancer to develop — the epidemic began.

SMOKING AND THE PUBLIC INTEREST

THE MODERN CIGARETTE. The first step toward the modern cigarette was the invention, in the 1880s, of a cigarette machine which was capable of outproducing the hand-rollers hundreds of times over. Early manufacturers thought that consumers wouldn't take to a machine-made cigarette — with the notable exception of James B. Duke. Duke's American Tobacco Company, or the Tobacco Trust, as it was soon called, gradually took over first the cigarette and then almost the entire tobacco business, with the exception of cigars (they are manufactured, to this day, by a fairly splintered industry). By 1910 the American Tobacco Company had control of 86 per cent of the cigarette business, 85 per cent of the plug business, 76 per cent of the smoking tobacco business, and so on down the line of tobacco and related products.

In 1911, the U.S. Supreme Court, under the Sherman Anti-Trust Act, broke up the Tobacco Trust into competing companies. The four that concern us here are American, Liggett & Myers, P. Lorillard, and Reynolds. American was by far the largest after the dissolution; it got cigarettes in all prices and types. Liggett and Lorillard were awarded more limited markets. Reynolds, confined to chewing tobacco, fatefully was given no cigarette business at all.

Reynolds' search for a cigarette competitor led to the *Camel*, introduced in 1913. Its ancestor, despite the dromedary on the package, was pipe tobacco made of flavored burley. The *Camel* combined burley, a dark heavy tobacco that could absorb flavorings, flue-cured tobacco for lightness and bite, a small amount of Maryland for its burning propensities, and Turkish for aroma. The public acceptance of this new mixture was nothing short of phenomenal, and not until the massive switch to filters would the industry see such a change again. *Camels* accounted for a third of American cigarette sales by 1917, and 45 per cent by 1923. The other companies swung into line,

126

American with *Lucky Strike* and Liggett with *Chesterfield,* both based on the *Camel* formula of a burley blend.

By 1925, *Camels, Chesterfields,* and *Luckies* between them had over 80 per cent of the market and the cigarette business was fixed in the pattern it would keep until the early 1950s, when the "health scare" turned it inside out once more. Two other Reynolds concepts — putting cigarettes in packages of 20, and concentrating advertising on one brand — became standard practice for the industry. This, in turn, made it increasingly difficult for new competitors to enter the market because of the enormous advertising costs. Only three companies — Lorillard, with its comparatively late burley entry, *Old Gold;* Brown & Williamson, a subsidiary of the British-American Tobacco Company, itself once part of the old Tobacco Trust, with *Raleighs* and a few others; and Philip Morris, with its cigarette of the same name — made any headway at all. The leaders fought for position in the market; *Luckies* and *Camels* interchanged as first and *Chesterfields* fought to catch up. But an American cigarette meant one of a handful of brands, all straights, two-and-one-half inches long, fairly similar in strength and taste. These cigarettes seduced millions of people away from other tobacco products, and more millions, when they began to use tobacco, started with them.

THE "AS IF" RESPONSE. One of the oddities of the present smoking situation is that while neither manufacturer nor customer wants to admit that the health charges are true, both have acted as if they are. The "as if" response, if it may be called that, has utterly changed the cigarette business. So different are today's cigarette products from those of the past that Stephan E. Wrather, director of the Tobacco Division, Agricultural Marketing Service, U.S. Department of Agriculture, declares that "millions of new or younger smokers have never

127

been exposed to what older Americans think of as a genuine cigarette."

About 75 per cent of all U.S. cigarette sales, and three of the four major types produced, are now in cigarettes that barely counted before the health scare began — king-size straights, filtered cigarettes, and mentholated filter types. Filtered cigarettes, including menthols, account for more than half of sales, and the expectation is that three out of four cigarettes sold eventually will be filters. Mentholated filters are the newest beneficiaries of the health charges and the fastest growing of cigarette types. The old regulars, *Luckies, Camels, Chesterfields* and the rest, now account for only a quarter of industry sales, and they are moving steadily down.

Always loathe to mention cigarettes and health in the same breath, industry executives have tried to account for the rise of filters by saying that people like them because they keep tobacco out of the mouth, or that mass swings in taste are inexplicable and recent developments are merely another in a long line of such changes. But the fact is that in only a few years 35,000,000 smokers have begun using cigarettes that are harder to inhale, less aromatic, and yield less of a kick; one hardly needs to labor the point. No one has proved the filter to be an adequate health safeguard (but see page 96); it does, however, allow the smoker to rationalize the habit.

Within the industry, the smoker's search for safety has changed practices of long standing. It has made a difference in the type of leaf purchased, for the manufacturer can use in filter cigarettes cheaper and stronger parts of the plant, and this has had a deep effect on growers. It has reversed the trend toward a single sales leader — each company is now obliged to have a "department store" of cigarettes, a brand in each of the four categories, straights, king-size, filtered, and filtered-mentholated, and sometimes more than one brand in a category, so that its products are competing with each other. It has meant much higher advertising costs, large development costs for new brands, promotional campaigns to get vendors to take new brands on their already crowded shelves, and sometimes lower profits despite record sales.

Success or failure in the cigarette business depending, as it does, on a correct appraisal of a public reaction to a problem which the industry is reluctant to mention, the cigarette companies are in a rather mysterious competitive situation, and each has gone its own way in the dark. American, with strong entries in both the regular and king-size races, has been slow-moving in filters. This may be one reason it has fallen behind Reynolds in total sales. Reynolds, powerful in everything but kings, is the industry sales leader. Liggett & Myers has suffered because its *L&M* filter sales have lagged, and the company admits it made a mistake not to give its king-size *Chesterfields* a different name. Lorillard is now the "house of filters," and behind its *Kent* the company has surged. Philip Morris is committed to filters to the extent that over 90 per cent of its cigarette sales are in products it didn't make 10 years ago. Brown & Williamson, with seven brands of cigarettes — more than any other manufacturer — seems to be seeking out the nuances in the smoker's present uncertain mood.

Another example of the "as if" response is that most cigarette companies now emphasize the research they are doing, although the dread word "health" is never used. Lorillard scientists managed to write a long report on removing phenols by filtration without ever mentioning "lungs." Liggett spent some years and millions of dollars developing a new brand, *Lark*. Philip Morris says that it is capable of taking various substances out of smoke. Because of company secrecy, it is impossible to say just what kind of research is underway in company laboratories. In the view of some medical men, company research is confined to removing substances from smoke, and does not take in a study of the problem of cigarettes and disease. "We are not in the cancer research business," Benjamin H. Few, former president of Liggett & Myers, has said. "Our business is the study of our product."

A final example of the "as if" response is that the companies are diversifying. It may be the way of industry today, but for the cigarette companies diversification has come late in the game and in the face of much evidence that smokers are giving cigarettes a second look. Reynolds has an aluminum products division and a fruit juice company, Lorillard is in tin, and Philip Morris, which does 20 per cent of its business in noncigarette products, is in razor blades and packaging. The other companies say that they, too, want to diversify. It would seem to be a good way of hedging their bets.

*"And even at that we don't have
King size in mentholated and flip-top-box filters."*

CHAPTER 11
The Search for a Villain

A SIGN of high intelligence, it has been observed, is the ability to hold two contradictory ideas in mind at the same time, and if this is true the American cigarette industry must be credited with extraordinary mental powers. In practice — that is, on the realistic level of giving customers what they seem to want — the industry has been entirely flexible on the health issue. But when it comes to public statements, to an intellectual position on the matter, the industry has been rigid, even defiant. "In these days of crisis in Cuba, India, West Berlin and way stations," said Howard S. Cullman, president of Cullman Brothers, a cigar leaf company, "we should give our grateful thanks that the problems of the industry are of minor significance. Like the measles, we have recurrent attacks of do-gooders who want to attack the pleasures of life, be it drinking, smoking or even Arthur Murray dancers. . . . We have had too many 'statisticators' during the past few years announcing what they think should be our way of life, our pleasure and our habits. Unfortunately, in many instances there is a commercial tinge thereto."

It is not clear about the tinge; it was clear, though, that Mr. Cullman wanted to hold *somebody* responsible for the nasty business about health. In this, he was close to the trade publication, *Tobacco Leaf*, which in 1953 was muttering darkly,

". . . these attacks have become more frequent and menacing in character. Such magazines as *The Reader's Digest*, the *Christian Herald* and others have become sounding boards for the opinions of certain so-called medical scientists who profess to find in tobacco a cause of disease. These attacks are addressed to the medical, social and religious animosities and prejudices of the country, and the moribund alcohol-obsessed temperance movement has taken them to its bosom as something extremely touching." Moreover, said *Tobacco Leaf* in 1954, ". . . we are more than ever convinced that the medico-admanstock tipster assault on cigarettes and the value of cigarette company securities is premeditated and planned propaganda." Another trade publication, *Tobacco*, which bills itself as "The Most Useful Paper," was shocked at the "apparent willingness of public figures to abandon perspective in order to cash in on publicity." And to *Tobacco Leaf*, Senator Maurine Neuberger, a proponent of tar and nicotine labeling and other measures, was a "violent antibac," carrying on a "personal vendetta against the tobacco industry."

None of this suggests a high degree of realism. Since 1953 the cigarette industry has been searching hard for someone to blame, on the theory that villainy is afoot. It is another way of denying the validity of the health charges, for if the opposition is biased and has motives of its own, then the charges are hardly objective. After casting about, the industry seemed to have settled on two principal sources of opposition — "warriors against pleasure," and the American Cancer Society.

E. A. Darr, former president of Reynolds, has said that the American Cancer Society is out to "destroy the cigarette industry." To Arthur Y. Lloyd, of the Burley and Dark Leaf Tobacco Export Association, "The American Cancer Society relies almost wholly upon health scare propaganda to raise millions of dollars from a gullible public." "The March phenomenon of the discovery of new statistical evidence finding smoking to cause lung cancer occurred again in 1962, making it the eighth year in a row for the spectacle," said *Tobacco Leaf*. "This time it was the Royal College of Physicians in London which came up with the data necessary to give impetus to the annual fund raising drive of the American Cancer Society." (The American Cancer Society insists that it has refused to exploit the cigarette-lung cancer relationship for fund raising. It has also said that it is not anti-cigarette but anti-cancer, and would be delighted with a safe cigarette.)

Further evidence of jittery nerves among cigarette people came in *Tobacco Leaf's* warning that unscrupulous people were preparing products like confections and instant shoeshine kits that would fit in cigarette vending machines. And the National Association of Tobacco Distributors said not long ago, "Unfortunately, during the last dozen years, the most concentrated anti-tobacco 'campaign' in nearly half a millenium of abuse and vilification has produced so many warped and distorted headline stories, that it's quite impossible for an uninformed tobacco salesman to go around without an inferiority complex about his job, if he hasn't had a chance to check the full truth of the other side of the smoking picture."

THE TOBACCO INSTITUTE. To tell that side more forcefully, the tobacco industry in 1958 set up the Tobacco Institute — "to promote better public understanding of the tobacco industry and its place in the national economy and to compile and disseminate information relating to the industry and the use of tobacco products."

The Tobacco Institute's public relations advisor, it turned out, was again Hill & Knowlton. (The Tobacco Institute is itself a public relations organization, and as if this were not already quite a lot of public relations, most cigarette compa-

133

nies also retain their own public relations firms.) The Institute consists of 12 tobacco product manufacturers, including Liggett & Myers, which did not join the T.I.R.C. Participation in either group does not come cheap. The president of Liggett & Myers said recently that his company's annual contribution to the Institute was $150,000, and Lorillard said its was $100,000.

The Tobacco Institute was active in a change in the system for affixing tax stamps and it promoted tobacco's 350th anniversary in the U.S. It tries hard to establish the traditional place of tobacco in American culture and issues pamphlets on the history of tobacco in various states. It sends out news release saying, for instance, that tobacco is the "last stronghold of the family farm" and that tobacco products give employment to 17,000,000 Americans, a questionable figure unless "employment" is taken to include having a cigarette machine at a gas station. On taxes it takes a dual stance: on the one hand, it implies, the government could barely function without tobacco taxes, but on the other it complains that these taxes are too high.

But such activities seem secondary to the health issue, and here one wonders why the industry needs both the T.I.R.C. and the T.I., since they say exactly the same things. "There have always been a few people who are fanatically prejudiced against tobacco," said James P. Richards, former President of the Institute and a Congressman from South Carolina before that. Richards was striking the villain theme. "Not liking it themselves, they are oppposed to its use by others." Richards may have had the same speech writer as Edward F. Ragland, the Institute's vice-president: "[The statistical evidence] was promptly taken up by the anti-tobacco crusaders — those people who, not liking it themselves, want to deny its use to others." The present president, George V. Allen, head of the U.S. Information Agency under Eisenhower, and a native of

North Carolina, says that "We must learn to distinguish the real facts about tobacco from unjustified emotional campaigns, based on the 'health scare' technique — a technique that was not successful 100 or 300 years ago, and, we are confident, will not be successful today."

A registered lobbyist on the Institute's staff has done little so far, a Hill & Knowlton spokesman said, "because there have been no bills to fight." But an indication of how the Institute would react to possible legislation came in its response to the suggestion that cigarettes be labelled according to tar and nicotine content. "The suggestion," Allen said, "is not feasible. We are determined to ascertain scientific facts before reaching conclusions. Labeling legislation is not justified in the absence of adequate scientific information." (Actually, one of the Institute members does label its cigarettes, though Allen may not know it. G. A. Georgopulo & Co., the smallest cigarette manufacturer in the U.S., puts tar and nicotine contents on its *Turkish Delights* because it thinks they are significantly low.)

When and if serious cigarette legislation becomes an active prospect, one can expect that the Tobacco Institute will become a rallying point for the tobacco interests and whatever legislative support they can find.

But the main danger for the companies may be in the form of suits from those who have contracted lung cancer and blame it on cigarettes. An indication of the kind of opposition they are likely to face comes from Melvin M. Belli, a lawyer noted for successful damage suits. "In the cancer cigarette cases, so-called," Belli wrote in 1958, "the impotency of the law through its delay is even more apparent, perhaps, than in any other modern case... years have gone by before a case actually has been presented to a jury.... In the meantime, magazines, radio, television, billboard, newspaper and other media of advertising continue whisperingly and willfully to

135

misrepresent and deny subtly and adroitly what the great weight of scientific evidence has proved beyond reasonable doubt, the causality between smoking and cancer."

There are those who feel that the cigarette companies will be in deep trouble the moment a jury awards, and a court sustains, major damages to a lung cancer victim or his heirs. The prospects with respect to this, and a discussion of what has already happened, are taken up in Part III, Chapter 14.

THE ECONOMICS OF TOBACCO. Upwards of 6,000,000 people are involved in the tobacco business, though not full-time by any means. The cigarette industry employs directly somewhere in the neighborhood of 40,000 people, the majority of whom are in manufacturing, which is highly automated. About 3,000,000 derive a substantial part of their income through retail sales — that is, through retail outlets for which tobacco is more than just a casual item. About 300,000 people own stock in tobacco corporations. There are 190,000 farms that have more than half of their output in tobacco, the Department of Commerce says, but the Department of Agriculture says that there are 700,000 farm families who have tobacco as a principal cash crop, and estimates the tobacco-farm population at about 3,000,000. Tobacco products are an important U.S. export — 24 billion cigarettes were sold abroad last year, and one-fourth of the leaf grown is exported, for a value of nearly $500 million.

It would seem that a country as large and prosperous as ours could absorb whatever setbacks the tobacco industry might have, but there are two especially sensitive areas in the tobacco economic picture. One of them is the farmers. Tobacco, intensively cultivated, is grown on farms averaging three acres, not adaptable to extensive farming. Nonetheless, in several tobacco-producing states, there have been public suggestions that farmers begin to diversify. As we noted earlier, the companies have been doing this for some time.

"If it reached a point where you had to curtail production, and this is a serious possibility," Mr. Wrather of the Department of Agriculture has said, "the question would be what to do with the labor and how to find other cash crops. I don't know what we're faced with — we're perhaps losing smokers in the upper age brackets and replacing them with younger ones. So far, there has been no significant loss to the government under the price support program, but we are getting into trouble as a result of the high supply of tobacco. If the utilization of tobacco is further aggravated by the health problem, the government would take a sizable loss."

The other trouble area is taxes; there is no doubt that tobacco taxes do make a sizeable contribution, over $3 billion in 1962 in Federal, state, and local taxes. Ways and means, certainly, would have to be found to replace this revenue if tobacco sales should slip. The high tax take, meantime, and also the agricultural support program could involve the government in a contradiction if it should enlist actively on the side of those trying to do something about smoking as a health problem. Legislation aimed at smoking is conceivable and even likely; it is certainly one of the things the industry most fears. But the government has had experience with the inconsistency of collecting from an industry while imposing restrictions on its products; it has been doing just this with the liquor industry for a long time.

At this writing cigarette sales among older people are leveling off, and the industry admits that it may have reached a saturation point in sales to adults. Its big hopes, then, are the enormous generation of war babies, just now reaching smoking age, and overseas sales. But both hopes are cloudy. The youthful market, which has been the industry's major advertising target for years (as Part III recites in some detail), is the area in which legislation of some kind is most probable. And foreign countries are hardly less aware of the health hazards of smoking than we are; many have already taken remedial steps, some of which are outlined and discussed in Part IV.

"We cannot afford to fear economic consequences to business interests," Viscount Hailsham, British Minister of Science, said in a recent speech in the House of Lords. "Men who go into business for profit must be prepared, if necessary, to bear loss. This is one of the advantages of the private enterprise system." But the cigarette industry has had little experience with this particular advantage of the private enterprise system; unlike most industries, it has never had an annual loss. Perhaps it is that simple fact which explains why the industry can continue to conduct itself, at least in public, as though nothing really serious has been happening.

CHOICES AND CONSEQUENCES. Let us return to the choices for the industry suggested at the beginning of this Part II, but look at them now in the context of 1963. So little dispute remains among medical men and researchers about the validity of the health charges that it seems almost idle to discuss them. As we have seen, finding upon finding has piled up. But it was unlikely then, and it is unlikely now, that manufacturers would stop making their product. At the other extreme, the manufacturers certainly can't afford to ignore the charges. That still leaves the choice between an open admission that cigarettes are a health hazard (accompanied by the intent to do whatever is possible and to cooperate with others in every way) and a continuing policy of denials (accompanied by the sowing of confusion among the general public).

"... I regret the present professed agnosticism on the part of the tobacco trade," Lord Hailsham said in his House of Lords speech, words that would pertain equally to American

138

tobacco interests. "It is not that I condemn them. It is not that I criticise them in any way, save this one. On the contrary, I realise that it must be a hard and bitter thing to persuade oneself that an honourable business, decently built up, is in fact purveying a substance capable of implanting mortal disease without any fault on the part of the purveyor. But the facts of life are often hard things to face, and the impression the tobacco manufacturers now make on public opinion — this I must tell them plainly — will largely depend on the extent to which they prove themselves able to recognise as facts propositions which are accepted by impartial scientists everywhere but which they find so unpalatable."

There are those who think that what has happened so far has had its beneficial aspects. Lewis Gilbert, the well-known representative of small stockholders, says, "No matter which way it turns out it has been for the best. The cigarette companies have been encouraged to do medical research they would never have done otherwise." Dr. Kotin, member of the Scientific Advisory Board of the T.I.R.C., is pleased with the research done by that group. Still, Kotin says, "If they'd come to me at the beginning I would have said to give the money to an impartial research organization like the National Research Council. I'd still say it."

Stuart A. Mayer, associate professor of chemistry at the University of Bridgeport, has written, "It seems to me that if the tobacco industry were really concerned with the public interest it would, in accord with the mass of scientific evidence, display on each pack of cigarettes the modest statement: Excessive use may lead to lung cancer. . . ." And a spokesman for the American Cancer Society has said, "We think the industry's public relations response has been stupid. They ought to admit that there is a connection between smoking and health and do something about it."

To return to Lord Hailsham, "I believe, with absolute conviction, that this evidence is compelling, and that not to accept it is not so much to sin against the light as to disregard one's own long-term interests. I am quite sure myself that it would in the end be more to their credit and less to their disadvantage if they got together in their board rooms and frankly recognised that the merchandise they are now selling, in this present form, is dangerous and, taken to any degree of excess, potentially lethal. If they would do that they could begin to plan the consequences, which it is absolutely vital for them to plan, and if they do not plan now in advance of the recognition of the facts they will find it very much to their disadvantage."

To Cameron Day, *Printers' Ink*'s managing editor, "The cigarette companies have pushed themselves into a bad position. We don't know what they can do but they must do something. They have been waiting for a miracle — hoping that the problem will solve itself — but it isn't likely to get better; in all probability, it will get worse."

The reality of the industry's present situation does seem to be of this nature. Whether the cigarette companies can summon whatever it will take them to face up to the reality is another matter. On the record to date, the chances do not seem glowing.

PART III
The Industry:
Advertising & Health

Lucky Strike question and answer—1932

CHAPTER 12
The Tar Derby: Before, During, and Since

THE CIGARETTE INDUSTRY, *Business Week* once observed, is a classic example of how a mass-production industry is built on advertising. "Unfortunately," *Business Week* went on to say, "the cigarette companies achieved much of this remarkable result by screaming at the top of their lungs about nicotine, cigarette hangovers, smoker's cough, mildness, and kindred subjects." In one way or another, health is a theme which has been at the center of cigarette advertising from the very beginning. The introductory campaign for the cigarette which opened the industry's modern era, *Camels*, got across the point that there was something less harmful about this brand; its specially selected Turkish and domestic tobaccos did not bite the tongue or leave a *cigaretty* taste in the mouth, the copy explained, and added, "You know what *that* means!"

From the time of the first *Camel* campaign in the early years of the century on into the 1950s, the ways in which the companies used and misused health appeals to build sales were endless, ingenious, and not without their funny side. When *Lucky Strike* set out to fight *Camel* for sales leadership almost two generations ago, it did so with European opera singers who reported to the New World, "I Protect My Precious Voice with *Lucky Strikes.*" Those were the days when health was a

143

positive appeal in cigarette advertising. In one of the most successful of all advertising campaigns, American women were urged to "reach for a *Lucky* instead of a sweet." Sales of *Lucky Strike* jumped more than 300 per cent in one year and the health appeal was promptly broadened and imitated. *Luckies* were the favorites of many athletes ("who must keep in good shape"); there was "Not a Cough in a Carload of *Old Golds*"; one could smoke as many *Camels* as one wanted, and they would never get on one's nerves. "Do You Inhale?" inquired *Lucky Strike*. "What's there to be afraid of?"

As Consumers Union pointed out in its first test report on cigarettes, which appeared in the July 1938 issue of CONSUMER REPORTS: "There is little difference perceptible between the various brands of any one type of cigarette . . . none of the popularly advertised brands appears to be more harmful than any of the others. . . . Cigarette advertising, fighting hard to deny this sameness, is generally misleading, often false, and most of the time laughable."

But such comments were appropriate to another and more comfortable time. After the evidence began coming in on the lung cancer link, the health claims in cigarette advertising ceased to be funny. As the evidence continued to build, the companies tried to outshout it more and more shrilly — until, at last, a breaking point of sorts was reached. In 1960, during closed-door negotiations with the Federal Trade Commission in Washington, the cigarette manufacturers agreed to call off what had come to be known as the "Tar Derby" — the race to be up front with the least tars, the best filter, the most "filter traps." The move was billed in the trade press as heralding a "dramatic and drastic change in cigarette advertising."

From the perspective of three years later the change does not seem either drastic or dramatic. It is true that the heavy "laboratory test" promotions, the strident "lowest in tars"

144

claims, and the most pretentious of the "smoke-our-brand-and-stay-well-it's-those-other-brands-that-hurt-you" campaigns have been put aside. This is to say that the most extreme of the industry's exploitations of the health issue have subsided, at least for the most part and at least for the time being; unfortunately, legitimate information on tar and nicotine content has subsided, too, while the health appeals continue, in pleasanter guise. The symbol of cigarette advertising since the end of the Tar Derby has been the robust young man lighting up, the radiantly healthy couple strolling among fountains and waterfalls, firm hand in firm hand. This is more soothing than the old outrages of cigarette advertising; it is subtler; and as an advertising approach to the exigencies of the present, it is probably more effective.

Moreover, by calling off the infighting that characterized the Tar Derby, the cigarette industry succeeded in extricating itself from the embarrassing position it had occupied since the health disclosures of the early 1950s — that of constantly reminding its customers through its own advertising that cigarettes carried a real threat to their health.

CIGARETTES AND THE FTC. For all the excesses of cigarette advertising from the time of World War I to the beginning of World War II — the formative years of the industry — the Federal Trade Commission took no formal action against any of the major companies. By the time it did take action against *Lucky Strikes and Pall Malls* in 1942, cigarette advertising had become so widely identified with nonsense in the public mind that, for many, regulatory action seemed a little pointless. And so it turned out to be, although for different reasons. Over the next decade the FTC proceeded against every major tobacco company at least once; against the claims for *Camel* that it aided digestion, relieved fatigue, and never irritated the throat; against the claims for *Lucky Strike* that "with independent tobacco experts . . . it's *Luckies* 2 to 1;" against the claim for *Pall Mall* that it filtered the smoke in such a way as to get rid of throat irritants; against the claim for *Old Gold* that it had less nicotine and tars than other brands; against the claim for *Philip Morris* that it was less irritating to the upper respiratory tract; against the claim for *Chesterfield* that it would not harm the nose and throat; against the claim for *Kool* that it gave protection against colds.

What emerged, as the FTC tried to push through its actions and the companies resisted, was the fundamental incapacity of the regulatory agency to regulate. It was stymied by the law itself, by its own administrative procedures, and by the adept delaying tactics of the lawyers for the companies. By the time a complaint took effect, the objectionable advertising claims had generally been retired from overuse. Like astronomers studying stars millions of light-years away, the FTC commissioners were constantly coming to conclusions about phenomena that were no longer in existence.

In August of 1942, for example, the Commission charged Philip Morris with advertising falsely that its cigarettes were less irritating than other brands. Philip Morris attributed its specialness to its use of diethylene glycol instead of glycerine as a moistening agent, and it martyred many rabbits in the course of demonstrating its claim. The FTC remained unimpressed, however, and in 1952, ten years after the original charge had been filed, it forbade the company from claiming that the brand was recommended by "outstanding nose and throat specialists." But in 1953 Philip Morris was still telling the nation to "STOP WORRYING" about cigarette irritation and to "Remember: PHILIP MORRIS AND ONLY PHILIP MORRIS . . . IS *ENTIRELY FREE* OF IRRITATION USED IN *ALL OTHER* LEADING CIGARETTES!" The case

146

dragged on until March of 1955, when the Commission dismissed its complaint on the ground that the company had stopped using both the "less irritating" theme and the moistening agent on which it was based.

There were strong objections at first to the FTC's invasion of the domain of the cigarette advertisers, and no doubt some of these objections reflected honest outrage. The makers of *Lucky Strike* protested that their claims were not really false, and that it was dangerous to allow a bureaucratic commission to judge what was "significant" in an advertiser's claims. (On hearing this, the editors of *Commonweal* could not control a certain impatience: "... it rubs us the wrong way to see the American Tobacco Company — an outfit that has done its best for years to beat the human brain into a sensitive and helpless state of nervous exhaustion — setting up its defense now on the high mental ground of 'truth,' just as though it knew the lay of the land.")

But as the years passed it became clear that the companies, aware of the FTC's lack of power, were willing to take their chances. At worst, there might be a fine to contend with. It was found, for example, that the actual difference in nicotine content between *Old Gold* and other brands tested by *Reader's Digest* in 1942 was 1/177,187th of an ounce per cigarette. By smoking a pack of *Old Golds* every day for a year, a cautious man could ingest 1/24th of an ounce less nicotine. *Reader's Digest* had correctly stated that differences of this order were not significant; *Old Gold* nevertheless trumpeted "*Old Gold* Lowest in Nicotine"; the FTC moved in with a complaint. So *Old Gold* changed its theme: "No other leading cigarette is less irritating or easier on the throat, or contains less nicotine than *Old Gold*. This conclusion was established on evidence by the United States Government." Such assays in semantics eventually, years later, earned P. Lorillard a $40,000 fine, less

147

than the cost of one color advertising page in *Life*. And that was one of the biggest fines ever levied in a case of this kind.

When the FTC tried to speed up its legal proceedings in the fall of 1952 by skipping the preliminaries and going directly to court for a temporary injunction against a *Chesterfield* campaign, it was turned down. The Commission's argument was that since the *Chesterfield* advertising was discussing the effects of tobacco on the nose and throat — with the aid of X-ray pictures and reports of medical examinations — it should be treated as drug advertising, an area in which the FTC could sometimes use injunctive powers. Judge Irving R. Kaufman of the District Court for the Southern District of New York ruled that tobacco had not been intended by Congress to fall under the category of a drug. The FTC appealed the decision, lost, and returned to its old, time-devouring procedures.

The record of the FTC with the cigarette industry up to the early 1950s was thus one of inaction for many years and futile action for many more. As the cancer evidence began piling up in 1952, the FTC relapsed into semi-inaction (though with some exceptions to be noted further on); it aroused itself in 1959 and 1960 for the industry negotiations which ended the Tar Derby. And whether it did well or badly there — indeed, whether in the final analysis it acted or was acted on — is still a matter for speculation.

The FTC is certainly one of the arms of government which should be made to serve the public interest in meeting the now deadly serious cigarette-health problem (for more on this, see Part IV). Any agency in the regulatory role of the FTC must offer this possibility; but the record here is not promising.

CHAPTER 13
Kings and Filters

THE SITUATION facing cigarette makers at the turning point of ten years ago was worrisome but not without its bright side from an industry point of view. Most people in the country over the age of 18 smoked, despite many years of warnings that the habit wasn't good for them. There was every reason to believe that they would continue to smoke unless the tobacco promoters scared them out of their wits. The problem, for the advertisers, was to re-examine how the smoker now looked at cigarettes, and motivational researcher Dr. Ernest Dichter told them that the advertiser who seemed to be helping the smoker in any new assessment of his habit would have a competitive edge. The task was to demonstrate that the manufacturer was on the side of the customer.

For how to accomplish this, the manufacturer of cigarettes had only to look at his sales charts; it was apparent there that king-size and filtered cigarettes were doing exceedingly well. In 1953 four of the ten best-selling cigarettes in the country were king-size, and *Fortune* predicted in December that "the long cigarette that protects the throat is well on the way to industry dominance."

But not all of these kings were destined to be crowned. It became clearer each year that the heir apparent to the sales throne was the filter cigarette, with or without the king's

149

length as a part of it. The first company to get in on the potentialities of this awakening market was P. Lorillard, which introduced its *Kent* in 1952 with an unusually heavy promotion campaign that played hard on the virtues of its Micronite filter, "developed by researchers in atomic-energy plants." In 1953 the sales of *Kents* went up four-fold.

As already noted in Part II, Lorillard was not left to the solitary enjoyment of such a boom. "Chemists say filter-tip cigarettes can't be made with less irritating factors than *Chesterfield*," said Benjamin H. Few, then Ligget & Myers president; he added, "But if the public wants it, so long as it isn't harmful, we'll give the public what it wants. . . . If *Chesterfield* consumption is to be drained off by king-size, filter-tip cigarettes, let it be by our own brands." And so *L&M* entered the lists. In 1953, Philip Morris bought Benson & Hedges and with it *Parliament*, in order to have a filter while its new *Marlboro* was being developed; Reynolds launched its king-size filter, *Winston*; and American Tobacco put a filter on king-size *Tareyton*. Since an established brand could get along with an advertising allocation of two cents a carton while a new entrant required 50 or 60 cents a carton or more to get off the ground, advertising costs moved up. They rose about 25 per cent from 1955 to 1956.

"The cigarette industry has emerged from the shadow of the cancer and heart disease scare," proclaimed *Business Week* in its 1955 review of the tobacco business. But tests of the new filter cigarettes made by Consumers Union showed that some of them yielded fully as much tar as the leading unfiltered brands. As the companies took to "re-engineering" their products, it became increasingly difficult to keep up with them. Of the major filter brands included in CU's 1955 tests, *L&M* with its Pure White Miracle Tip of Alpha-Cellulose ("just what the doctor ordered") came out with the lowest quantities of tar and nicotine. But in the 1957 tests, *L&M* was found to have gone up from 11 mg. of tar to 15 mg., and from 1.5 mg. of nicotine to 2.6 mg. Other cigarettes made similar swings (see Appendix C, page 217).

FUN AND SAFETY. In cigarette smoking, as in children's games, there seems to be an inverse ratio between fun and safety. The better the filter, the weaker the taste. Flavor becomes a function of risk. When, for instance, *Kents* were first introduced, their asbestos-like filters did such a good job that smokers found them hard to draw and not particularly flavorful when drawn — "like smoking through a mattress," a Lorillard man observed. In 1952, according to CU, a *Kent* gave off 0.5 mg. of nicotine and 2 mg. of tar. By 1955, Lorillard had made their cigarette more pleasurable by loosening up the filter, but in the process quadrupling its nicotine level and increasing its tar level sixfold. In 1957 CU found that *Kent* had quietly abandoned its highly publicized Micronite filter — "So safe, so pure, it's used to filter the air in leading hospitals" — for one that was very much like the commonly used cellulose tip, and the nicotine and tar in the smoke had gone up accordingly.

Once the cigarette makers discovered that they could get the tobacco flavor (the tars, that is) through a pretty good filter by using stronger grades of tobacco, those TV demonstrations of filter effectiveness took on less and less relevance. But even at their best — which at the time was not very good as far as the leading brands went — the filters provided highly uncertain protection. Persons who found that they were smoking more because they enjoyed filter tips less could easily wind up inhaling greater quantities of tars and nicotine than before. Since no one knew where precisely in the cigarette the cancer culprit resided, any implication that protection was to be found in one filter or another was highly speculative. A

CU representative had these doubts in mind when he told a Congressional Committee in 1957, "I believe that even when a company does not make any other claim than that it has a filter tip . . . it can be misleading."

Despite such objections, however, as the memory of their 1953-54 fright began to recede industry planners could draw breath more easily. In 1956 the Department of Agriculture reported that many people who had cut down on smoking had taken it up again, using mainly filter tips. Advertising men themselves were reacting much like everybody else; a survey of several hundred of them about this time found that half believed there was a "definite" or "possible" link between smoking and lung cancer.

Inspecting the again rising graph of cigarette sales at the close of 1956, the late Harry M. Wootten, long-time tobacco industry expert for *Printers' Ink*, rejoiced that "the smoking-and-health controversy . . . may be collapsing for lack of nourishment." His optimism was a reflection both of the cigarette men's wholehearted desire never again to hear the word cancer and of the realities of the market place. They were content to have people smoking filters just as long as they smoked something; and, it appeared, just as long as they smoked something, a great many people were content to smoke filters. In 1957 cigarette sales attained a new national record, at last topping their 1952 pre-scare peak.

But the achievement was a chaotic one, for steadily increasing medical evidence of the health hazards of smoking were being accompanied by steadily increasing claims of wonder-working filters, such as "400,000 Filter Traps!" and "Up to 43% Higher Filtration!" Early in 1958 a two-day conference of representatives of tobacco companies and testing laboratories (including Consumers Union), and FTC personnel concluded that a standard testing method for cigarettes which might clear up the conspicuously contradictory claims was practical. But no such test ever has been made official.

While every cigarette company had reason to be concerned lest a standard tar-nicotine test give grist to anti-tobacco mills, some had more special reasons for not welcoming it. For, they had to ask themselves, what was to happen to most of the brands on the market, including the best sellers, when there was but one authoritative and well-publicized standard by which to measure the presumable healthfulness of cigarettes? The president of R. J. Reynolds pooh-poohed the whole subject: "We attach no significance to the measurable quantities of solids and nicotines reported to have been found in the smoke of cigarettes."

Others, however, did attach significance to the tar-nicotine figures — or, at any rate, they continued to attach them to their ads. Toward the end of 1959, when the Tar Derby reached its climax, several new "ultra hi-filter" brands appeared on the market. They were relatively effective in reducing the tars and nicotine in their smoke, but they were even more effective in reducing the readers of the advertising to bewilderment. There was the new *Duke of Durham*, with its king-size filter, its recessed tip, its "air-cool" paper and its special blend of tobaccos which was "lowest in tars of all leading low-tar cigarettes." There was *Spring* — "lowest in tars, lowest in nicotine, lightest in menthol of all menthol cigarettes!" There was *Spud* — "Now lower in tars and nicotine than any leading cigarette." *Kent* and *Parliament* were still at it. And finally there was *Life*: "Your filter no longer filters best ... *Life* filters best by far."

LIFE AND MORALITY. In December 1959, the FTC, acting with notable speed, brought a formal complaint of misrepresentation against the Brown & Williamson Tobacco Corp. and the

Ted Bates Advertising Agency. Mainly, the FTC was annoyed by a TV commercial which claimed that *Life*'s filter ratings were "on file with the U.S. Government." Indeed they were, but the implication that this constituted an official warranty was unwarranted; the FTC had simply requested the data after the claim was made that *Life* had been "proved to give you the least tar and nicotine of all cigarettes."

In the course of justifying the *Life* campaign, Rosser Reeves, chairman of the board of the Ted Bates agency, enunciated a whole Madison Avenue morality: "The FTC may take exception to the phrasing and demonstration used in these advertisements," he said. "A difference of opinion is an understandable thing. But utterly apart from the phrasing used or the demonstration, what are the most important aspects of the totality of this advertising? If any person is led by the *Life* advertising to switch to *Life* cigarettes in the belief that it is the lowest in tars and nicotine — in truth and in fact he will be getting the cigarette with the lowest tars and nicotine ever on sale."

Reporting the story of the fast FTC action, CONSUMER REPORTS brooded over the likelihood that it would have the usual anticlimax: "It will be months, maybe years, before *Life* cigarettes can be forced to discontinue these claims, should the manufacturer choose to take advantage of the hearings, delays, injunctions and other legal maneuvers open to recalcitrant advertisers. Meanwhile *Life* goes on."

But *Life* did not go on for long. It died in the sudden ending of the whole Tar Derby at just this time. As the then Chairman of the FTC, Earl W. Kintner, told an advertising convention in Washington: In the absence of a satisfactory uniform test and proof of advantage to the smoker, "there will be no more tar and nicotine claims in advertising." The *Reader's Digest* promptly blamed the FTC for discouraging the manufacture of high-filtration cigarettes and for rescuing the smoker from chaos only to leave him in ignorance. A few months later, the American Cancer Society called on the Commission not only to allow the cigarette companies to publish figures on tar and nicotine content, but "to aid them in so doing" and to arrange promptly for a standard uniform test. Where Mr. Kintner had called the tar-and-nicotine blackout "a landmark example of industry-government cooperation in solving a pressing problem," the *Digest* quoted a Washington lawyer as saying it was "a landmark example of how bureaucrats solve a pressing problem by sweeping it under a rug."

The FTC has promised to review its ban on tar and nicotine advertising once the Surgeon General's Advisory Committee on Smoking and Health has made its report (see page 205). Meanwhile, it stays in effect, and smokers can only guess at what's going on in their cigarettes — as, for that matter, they had to guess when the advertisements were still shouting at them.

Chesterfield assurance—1954

CHAPTER 14

Health Claims and Damage Suits

THE HEALTH THEME that has nourished cigarette advertising for two generations may yet cause the industry considerable indisposition, since the companies' own health claims constitute much of the evidence produced against them in recent damage suits based on smoking and health.

The first cigarette-lung cancer case to be brought to trial by a victim (as distinct from heirs or an estate) was the suit, in 1960, of Otto Pritchard against Liggett & Myers. The plaintiff relied heavily on previous advertising claims by the defendant, such as a 1934 advertisement saying that "A good cigarette can cause no ills and cure no ailments . . . but it gives you a lot of pleasure, peace of mind and comfort. . . . There is no purer cigarette than *Chesterfields.*" Also cited was the statement by Arthur Godfrey on the air in 1952, the year that saw the first serious indictment of cigarette smoking in relation to lung cancer: "You hear stuff all the time about 'cigarettes are harmful to you' and this and that and the other thing. . . . Here's an ad, you've seen it. If you smoke, it will make you feel better, really. 'Nose, throat and accessory organs not adversely affected by smoking *Chesterfields.*' This is the first such report published about any cigarette. A responsible consulting organization has reported the results of a continuing study by a competent medical specialist and his staff on the effects of smoking *Chesterfield* cigarettes." (This was part of the campaign against which the FTC tried unsuccessfully to obtain a drug injunction in 1952.)

Although Mr. Pritchard did not win his case, neither the cigarette makers nor their lawyers nor their advertising agencies are likely to miss the point of the U.S. Court of Appeals ruling, returning the case for jury trial after it had been dismissed by a District Court judge: "We think that the clear import of this advertising campaign was to lead smokers to believe that 'in order to play safe — smoke *Chesterfield.*' The plaintiff testified that he relied on these assurances, thinking that he would suffer no adverse effects from smoking *Chesterfields.* Whether it was reasonable for him to so rely was, of course, a matter for a jury. From the evidence, the jury could very well have concluded that there was a breach of an implied warranty of merchantability. If supported by the record, the District Court could charge the jury that they are to consider the practices of other cigarette manufacturers and the quality of cigarettes they manufacture as bearing on the question of merchantability." A jury finally decided against Mr. Pritchard apparently on the ground that while excessive smoking was one of the causes of his lung cancer, he had taken the risk on his own responsibility. (He subsequently died.)

The question of the scope of warranty, then, still hangs over the tobacco industry and its advertising. As U.S. Court of Appeals Judge Herbert F. Goodrich wrote in a supplementary opinion: "There is language in some of the advertisements for *Chesterfield* cigarettes shown in the evidence which could be understood to assert a claim on the defendant's part that these cigarettes are harmless. . . . If a manufacturer assures his potential public that his product is harmless and it is proved that it is not harmless, he can be held, no doubt, for breach of warranty. And when a person makes to another a statement

157

of fact which he does not know to be true, intending that the other shall act in reliance on the truth of that statement, he is liable for negligent misrepresentation. If the defendant here takes the position that nobody knows whether cigarettes cause cancer or not, but at the same time asserts to buyers that (its) cigarettes do not cause cancer, it is in difficulty if a customer shows that the use of these cigarettes caused cancer in him."

An outcome similar to that in the Pritchard case occurred in the $2 million suit of Edwin Green against the American Tobacco Company. Mr. Green, and later his heirs, brought suit in Florida against American Tobacco claiming that smoking *Lucky Strikes*, at the rate of between two and three packs a day, was the cause of his lung cancer. The jury found for the defendant, American Tobacco, its reasoning being 1) that Green's cancer of the left lung had caused his death, 2) that smoking *Lucky Strikes* was "a proximate or one of the proximate causes" of Green's cancer, but 3) that American Tobacco could not have known "on, or prior to February, 1956 [when Mr. Green's case was diagnosed] by the reasonable application of human skill and foresight" that cigarettes caused cancer.

Edwin Green's heirs appealed, their case turning on the point of American Tobacco's implied warranty that its product was safe. The Court of Appeals again held for the defendant, on the ground that the jury had found that American Tobacco could not have had "a superior opportunity to gain knowledge of the product and to form an opinion on its fitness."

THE LEGAL POSITION. The companies may be in a delicate legal position. For one thing, at least two juries *have* decided that cigarette smoking is a cause of lung cancer. *Tobacco*, referring to the Appeals Court's finding on the question in the Green case, said, "This is a disturbing ... decision. It could establish a dangerous precedent. Its implications are obvious and those who minimize them do a disservice to the tobacco industry."

If the principle that smoking may cause lung cancer is accepted by courts, other thorny matters of law are immediately raised, the first of which is the question of the implied warranty that cigarettes are fit for human consumption. Over the years the courts have shown a tendency to enlarge the meaning of implied warranty, to cover any product that appears in the market place. In the opinion of dissenting Judge J. Cameron in the Green case, "I do not think that one who warrants wholesomeness can escape liability by showing that it exercised reasonable care in its efforts to achieve it. Such an idea is, in my opinion, a refutation of the whole concept of warranty." And then, suppose a man began smoking heavily in, say, 1959, at the height of the Tar Derby — when most of the companies were implying that *other* brands were hard on health — and then died from lung cancer sometime during the 1960s? Could not a court rule that, by 1959, a cigarette company had indeed had a reasonable chance to learn about the hazardous nature of its product?

As State Senator H. Alva Brumfield of New Orleans has written, ". . . despite the abundance of warning signs, there has not been one warning by any tobacco company. It would appear manifest that tobacco companies were not only morally obligated, but legally and strictly bound to warn their customers that their products contained carcinogenic agents."

But the legal staffs of the cigarette companies feel that the decisions so far handed down have established precedents under which they will be exonerated in future trials, about 20 of which are now pending. Not only have judges and juries ruled that the companies couldn't have known their product was hazardous, but even if they had there would still be the question whether the smoker had the same knowledge and therefore smoked at his own risk.

As Chester Inwald, general counsel for the National Association for Tobacco Distributors, writes, "If the law of Florida may be taken as typical of the law of other states, we may safely conjecture that the basic problem of defending against cigarette lung cancer cases has been resolved in favor of producers and purveyors of cigarettes." But he adds: "If this is so, persons in the cigarette industry have only to fear the irresponsible consequences of their own conduct. Because it must be said that much of the difficulty which cigarette companies now encounter in law suits of this type is a direct result of advertising practices deliberately initiated by the cigarette companies themselves."

■ Just as this book went to press, the Florida Supreme Court, from which the Federal Court of Appeals had requested an advisory opinion, upheld Judge Cameron's dissent. The American Tobacco Company, said the court, was liable under Florida law even though the manufacturer could not have known that a smoker would be in danger of contracting lung cancer. Needless to say, this latest opinion undermines the basis for Mr. Inwald's optimism and suggests that the legal future of the cigarette companies may be a busier one than had been foreseen.

CHAPTER 15

The Drive for the Teen-age Market

WE HAVE NOT SEEN the last act of the fifty-year-long tragi comedy of cigarette advertising. Although domestic sales hit a record high of around a half trillion cigarettes in 1962, the rate of increase over the previous year was under 2 per cent, the lowest in five years. Profits were off slightly. And the U.S. Department of Commerce reports that per capita cigarette consumption actually declined in 1962, by about two cigarettes per smoker. If the advertisers are to keep on building sales they must attract new smokers; and the big potential is the teen-ager. There has been no problem tapping the teen-age market in the past; under ordinary conditions, there would be no problem today. But, as the publication of this book indicates, the times are far from ordinary for cigarettes, and today's advertising is going all out on youthful themes.

Not that this of itself is any innovation. The comic sections have had their share of cigarette ads in the past; 45-rpm rock-and-roll records have been used as cigarette promotion adjuncts; and the athletes and movie stars who have long puffed away on billboards across the land have generally been selected more for their appeal to the young of all ages than for their smoking preferences. On all these counts things are as before, only more so. And it is the "more so" that demonstrates the cigarette advertisers' concern.

For a good many years now, advertising expenditures for the major advertisers have been going up steadily. Moreover, the expense of establishing new brands and of renovating strategies for old ones has bitten deeply into profits. P. Lorillard, for example, had an exceptionally good year in 1962 by many measures; it passed the half-billion-dollar sales mark and displaced Liggett & Myers as the nation's third largest cigarette maker. But Lorillard's net profit declined by about $1.8 million; according to the company's annual report, this was "mainly due to the extraordinary expenses incurred in introducing *York* Imperial-size cigarettes nationally."*

Smoking has traditionally been one of the great experiments for fourteen-, fifteen-, and sixteen-year-olds; the youngster turning green over his first secret cigarette or pipe or cigar is a diverting character in American folklore. Today one high school student in three is a regular smoker, and almost one out of two seniors smokes regularly. The number of smokers between thirteen and nineteen, which has been on a gradual upward climb for years, took a particularly sharp rise between 1960 and 1962, jumping from 25 per cent to 35 per cent of the group.

These, then, are the people to whom the tobacco industry must look for its continued well-being. "Between the time a kid is eighteen and twenty-one, he's going to make the basic decision to smoke or not to smoke," says Liggett & Myers' vice-president and advertising director L. W. Bruff. "If he does decide to smoke, we want to get him." It is hard for a contemporary observer to escape the conclusion which *Fortune*

---

* The percentage of sales invested in advertising in 1959-60 by a broad sample of major industries included in an *Advertising Age* survey averaged out to about 1%. The percentage spent by tobacco manufacturers came to over 5%. In 1961 and again in 1962, the big six producers spent around $207 million to promote their products.

arrived at in 1963, that "cigarette ads often portray and seem to be pitched directly at young people."

A substantial majority of the substantial annual outlay of every cigarette advertiser goes to network and spot television and radio, and there is little on the air to send a fifteen-year-old away feeling he is not quite ready for it. The collection of comedians, cowboys, private eyes, romantic doctors and hero-athletes sponsored by the cigarette companies is fairly representative of television output and is as appealing to teen-agers as almost anything else available. The nation's two most popular medical shows, *Ben Casey* and *Dr. Kildare,* are both sponsored by tobacco firms.

Considering that every one of the big six cigarette makers was among the top 20 network TV advertisers in 1962, it must have seemed a stroke of unusual ingratitude when, in November 1962, the president of the National Association of Broadcasters, former Governor LeRoy Collins of Florida, brought his heavy charge against "the promotional impact of [cigarette] advertising designed primarily to influence young people." Hardly had he suggested that "the broadcaster should make corrective moves on his own," than the TV Bureau of Advertising and the Radio Advertising Bureau were circulating private memos to broadcasters, advising them to reassure the tobacco men that their advertisements were still welcome on the air. NBC and ABC felt called upon formally to disassociate themselves from Governor Collins' views, and CBS did so less formally.

"Understandably," *Television* wrote in 1962, "for the same reasons Macy's doesn't tell its shoppers that some of them are pushy, inconsiderate, potentially dangerous slobs, television has not emphasized the smoking-cancer hypothesis." The lack of emphasis *is* understandable. Still, two of the three major networks – CBS and, in a much lesser way, NBC – have produced reports on the subject of smoking and lung cancer. CBS did so effective a job on "The Teen-Age Smoker" in September 1962 that at least one advertiser, the American Tobacco Company, demanded equal time.

Our largest magazines, likewise beneficiaries of the cigarette advertiser's dollar, have not taken much editorial note of the subject, although they have not ignored it. Some years ago *Cosmopolitan* assigned a team of writers to do an article on environmental causes of cancer. After receiving the manuscript, the magazine's editors asked the writers to add a statement to the effect that the cigarette-lung cancer link was discredited. The writers declined, and requested that their names be taken off the story. Two paragraphs, written by someone else, were inserted, exonerating the cigarette as a cause of lung cancer, and the article was printed with a fictitious byline. A popular magazine article comparable in frankness to those that have appeared in the *Reader's Digest* — which now bars cigarette ads — was published by *Redbook* in June 1960, and *Redbook* is not known to have lost any cigarette advertising as a consequence. *Life* was chided for inconsistency by tobacco men some years ago after it ran a lung cancer story in an issue that contained three cigarette ads.

THE COLLEGE CAMPUS. Although high-school grounds are off limits to the cigarette seller, the college campus holds a special fascination for him, a fascination which has grown along with the growth of America's student body. And every element of the tobacco industry is alert to this burgeoning market. Back-to-school-time, as a sales executive informed tobacco distributors in July 1962, "is not without its tobacco potential" — a fact acknowledged by R. J. Reynolds with banners:

> WELCOME STUDENTS! LET'S GET ACQUAINTED
> WINSTON   SALEM

The president of the Student Marketing Institute, which specializes in selling things to students, observed in 1962, "The total cigarette marketing effort in the colleges has doubled in the last five years. Now everybody is in there slugging." For the tobacco merchants, slugging means paying campus representatives $50 a month to distribute samples. It means running contests, whose entries must be accompanied by empty packs. It means, in general, seeking to impress one's brand both on those currently using other brands and on the wholly uninitiated. For, in the amateur psychologizing of the director of Philip Morris' college sales department, "Students are tremendously loyal. If you catch them, they'll stick with you like glue because your brand reminds them of happy college days."

Mainly, cigarette slugging means advertising in campus newspapers. The National Advertising Service, Inc., advertising representative for 850 college papers throughout the country, proclaims that the average college student watches television only nine minutes a day, but reads every line of his school newspaper. "Never again," the Service's promotional literature warns businessmen, "will you reach them (college seniors) in a period where brand-changing is so rampant as it is in college years, when they are so eager to shake off family ties, so anxious to fill new needs and wants . . . ."

Some 20 different brands, representing every major company, are now promoted at colleges, and cigarette advertising accounts for an estimated 40 per cent of the national advertising that students find in their papers. The ads are as collegiate as the dirtiest pair of frosh buckskins. "Enter incessantly," urged Liggett & Myers when one of its recent contests was in full swing. "Because there are eight Sprites up for grabs, dad."

The facsimile of high sophomoric spirits in these ads cannot disguise their down-to-earth dollars-and-cents importance, both to the cigarette maker seeking fresh business among freshmen and to the campus paper seeking to exist without subsidy. Although some 200 of the papers signed up with National Advertising Service do not accept cigarette advertising, for most it is of outsize importance. In the fall of 1962, to cite a cautionary example, the editors of the New York City College evening session weekly, *Main Events*, decided to drop all cigarette advertising. Before the year was out, they had to appeal to the student body and to the school administration for assistance. The chastened editors expressed their regret that "the financial integrity of this paper — and apparently many other school papers across the country — must, to such a large extent, rely upon a product, which, according to the evidence, contributes so greatly to the death of thousands every year."

To the question of what part advertising plays in getting a boy or girl to sneak his or her first puff, one can obtain answers ranging from "insignificant" to "secondary" to "all-important," depending on which expert one chooses. The admen are caught in the dilemma of wanting their clients to believe that their efforts are powerful at the same time that they would like an increasingly suspicious public to dismiss them as being puny. Both their defenders and their detractors tend to assign them too much credit for controlling the human will. As Dr. Lester Breslow of the California State Department of Public Health reasonably points out, we must look for other reasons to explain the spread of cigarette smoking in countries where U.S.-style advertising does not prevail.

ADVERTISING AND SMOKING CUSTOMS. Whatever the precise contribution of advertising to our smoking customs, they do seem to represent social as well as personal satisfaction for the smoker, and cigarette advertisers have always recognized and played upon this dual draw. They have offered manliness to men, love to women, and sociability to everybody.

166

"The image we want for cigarettes is that they are used by a fun-loving group," says P. Lorillard's advertising director. It does not require Dr. Dichter to explain the attraction to teen-agers of good-looking, healthy-looking young couples lighting up companionably after a swim or at a picnic. "Smoking *Newports* is practically a vacation on the beach," an agency research man comments. "Smoking *Salems* is somewhat akin to a sexual romp in the woods." (One distinction between the explicit old-style health claims and the implicit new-style claims is that it would be far more difficult for a future lung-cancer victim to show that today's advertisements promised him long life.)

Advertising men often avow, in words similar to those of R. J. Reynolds' advertising manager, that "Cigarette advertising attempts to get smokers to switch brands, not to get new smokers." One major company's media director declares, "We have a very definite policy. We will not direct advertising primarily to those under the age of eighteen. Anybody over eighteen is fair game." A difficulty of this doctrine is that the ad which has an impact on a nineteen-year-old smoker cannot be depended upon to leave a fifteen-year-old non-smoker unmoved. What is the responsive age range, after all, to the American Tobacco Company's command to "Get Lucky — the taste to start with . . . the taste to stay with" — particularly when it is accompanied by photographs of an American League rookie and an Arizona deputy marshal?

More than a decade ago, when tremors of the oncoming crisis were just beginning to be felt in the tobacco industry, Dr. Dichter told cigarette makers that they were producing "a self-indulgence product." He told them that, while the American consumer indulged himself constantly with everything from soft drinks to hard liquor, he was still a Puritan at heart. To deal with this unprofitable Puritanism, Dr. Dichter developed his "first mechanism." As he explained, "I know that every time you sell a self-indulgence product, you are also confronted with the need of . . . well, of reassuring the guy that he is doing nothing sinful. You have to assuage his guilt feelings."

In recent years, other observers have questioned the desirability of assuaging a man's guilt about becoming habituated to a potentially dangerous product, and some have even ad-

"Every time you sell a self-indulgence product...." (Camel, 1936)

vised advertisers to look to their own sinfulness. In January 1963, the Rev. Neil Hurley delivered a strong attack in the Jesuit magazine, *America,* against TV commercials — he singled out those for cigarettes and beer — which aim at the teen-age market "by means of allusions to athletic prowess, popularity, datability and sexual allure." He was concerned not so much with the physical well-being of the TV viewer as with his

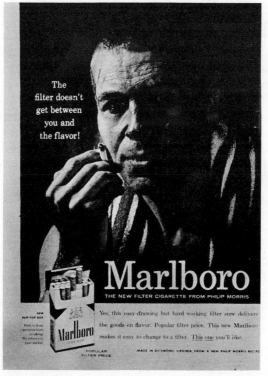

"...you have to assuage guilt feelings" (Marlboro, 1955)

spiritual well-being, with the possibility that an impressionable mind, or millions of impressionable minds, would come to accept the "hedonistic and epicurean system of values" relayed by the advertiser for the advertiser's benefit. He asserted that "the most successful advertising campaigns are those that overwhelm the senses," and went on: "The sultry woman's voice; the society setting; the rich, rough scion with the tattooed hairy hands; the attitude of complacency and apparent lack of anxiety — isn't this the typical TV approach for much cigarette advertising? It is basically a narcotic dream with an inexcusable dosage of dishonesty."

The work of criticizing this cigarette advertisement or that because it is false or misleading in one respect or another has been made trivial by the decade's events. The medical statistics force one to ask whether *any* kind of advertising for a product so intimately connected with disease can be condoned, and if so, then precisely what kind. Even if the testimonials of baseball player Roger Maris and golfer Arnold Palmer are true in all particulars, should they be used?

But it is in the American tradition to "advertise young" — unless you're trying to sell vintage wines or annuities or home sites in Florida — and the professionals seem to feel they have no choice but to continue to do so. In the past ten years, as we have seen, the cigarette companies have given ample demonstration of their willingness to ignore the health problem if it can be ignored and to exploit it if it can be exploited. It seems fair to conclude that they will not, and probably cannot, voluntarily and spontaneously regulate themselves.

PART IV
Points for a Program

GREAT BRITAIN

GREAT BRITAIN

DENMARK

SOVIET UNION ("He smokes—he quit")

CHAPTER 16
The Points of Approach

PART I OF THIS BOOK reviewed in some detail the very impressive evidence of the health hazards of smoking. Parts II and III searched the industry's record in the face of this evidence, finding no meaningful signs that the major health problem posed has been or will be adequately dealt with by the companies.

It is at this point that the problem becomes affected with a public interest.

A nationwide program to combat the health menace of cigarette smoking has been proposed by many; and signs accumulate steadily that some kind of broadly based program will be forthcoming. Consideration of some possible elements of such a program is the purpose of these final chapters.

Part IV draws from many sources, including the experience of the British, whose more critical situation with respect to the smoking-health problem has led them further into a drive against it. The member organizations of the International Office of Consumers Unions have furnished material on developments in their countries, and such material has been used in the pages that follow. The chapters of Part IV, which directly reflect and are shaped by the views of many of the people who have worked on this book, including the editors of

CONSUMER REPORTS, constitute a report to the public out of which, it is hoped, material and ideas may be mined in the public interest.

In the opinion of all concerned, any program capable of meeting the needs of the problem probably would have to take into account some or all of these seven approaches:

1. *Prohibition* of sales to minors, smoking by minors, sales through unattended vending machines, smoking in specified places – or other limited prohibitions.

2. The use of *taxation* to raise the price of cigarettes in order to discourage smoking through economic pressure on smokers, or the use of *selective taxation* to discourage the manufacture and sale of cigarettes with high nicotine and tar content.

3. The regulation of cigarette *labeling*, either to require a warning of possible damage to health, or to require that nicotine and tar content be specified, or both.

4. The regulation (or even outright prohibition) of cigarette *advertising*.

5. A program of *counter-advertising*, designed to make the public health hazards of cigarette smoking fully known to every man, woman, and child – and to keep these hazards as continuously present in the public consciousness as the pleasure of smoking is currently kept.

6. A program of *education* aimed squarely at elementary, high school, and college students.

7. A system of *clinics and other therapeutic aids* to help individual smokers or groups of smokers to stop smoking.

Some of these steps have already been taken in at least 23 countries and all were included in the program proposed for Great Britain by the Royal College of Physicians. On the pages that follow we will discuss these and related proposals in the light of current American conditions. Our discussion will not consider any *moral* objections to smoking. Neither will it be concerned (except indirectly at a few points) with *economic* considerations, nor with how the economic gap left by a gradual curtailment of smoking might be filled through other forms of enterprise. Such considerations can be very important, but cigarette smoking is now first and foremost a public health problem, and it is as such that we are concerned with it.

Particular emphasis will be placed on measures likely to minimize from now on the number of recruits attracted to smoking, especially from among children and adolescents. Among the stakes, let us remember, are the premature deaths from lung cancer of one million American children now in school.

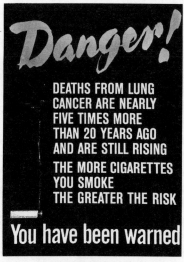

GREAT BRITAIN

CHAPTER 17
Prohibitions

THREE CENTURIES AGO, as we have already noted, the Czar of All the Russias prescribed nose-slitting and death for tobacco users.

Prior to 1922, 14 states had invoked legal penalties (though less drastic ones) against the smoking of cigarettes. By 1927 these laws were all repealed.

No responsible spokesman, of course, seriously proposes that cigarette smoking be made a criminal offense today — or even that the manufacture, sale, or possession of cigarettes be banned. The failure of the 18th Amendment outlawing alcoholic beverages is too fresh in memory; and the failure to control the use of narcotics by means of law enforcement is a further reminder that better ways must be found to achieve public health goals in a free society.

Partial prohibitions, however, may have a place in a broadfront approach to the smoking problem — for example, laws prohibiting the sale of cigarettes to minors. All of the states except Georgia, Louisiana, Texas, and Wisconsin now have such laws on their statute books, though enforcement is at best sporadic. In some states, too, children are forbidden by law to smoke in public.

A recent American Cancer Society study indicates that delaying the age at which a boy or girl starts smoking may be very important. Adults who start after 20 or 21, the new study suggests, smoke less in later years, inhale less, have fewer years of exposure, receive a smaller lifetime dose of carcinogens, and suffer less damage than do adults who started smoking earlier.

If cigarettes are to be kept out of the hands of minors, however, steps must be taken to curtail cigarette sales through vending machines, or at least through machines in unattended places where minors may have access to them. One English tobacco company has voluntarily moved in this direction. It has removed its own machines from sites accessible to children, and has refused to supply machines of other companies in such locations. England's Tobacco Advisory Council, a trade organization, has reminded all tobacco retailers that it is illegal for anyone under 16 to buy cigarettes, and has warned retailers to police their vending machines or risk their removal by court order.

Chicago already has banned unsupervised cigarette vending machines.

Many communities now prohibit the sale of liquor within a specified radius of a school. Cigarette sales might be similarly banned in such areas.

Almost everywhere, children and teachers alike are forbidden to smoke in classrooms. Finnish children are, in addition, forbidden to smoke on their way to and from school.

These and other measures to prevent sales to minors and smoking by minors may, however, have unanticipated consequences. Smoking is already for many children and adolescents a beguiling symbol of maturity, freedom, manliness, and womanliness; and for some children it is an expression of rebellion against adult restraints. The more effectively we ban smoking by children and young people, the more these attitudes toward cigarettes may be reinforced among them — and the more attractive smoking may therefore appear to them.

177

The price of preventing them from smoking while they are minors may be to increase the likelihood that they will smoke once they come of age.

Additionally, there are practical difficulties in enforcing such bans when so many adults are themselves unwilling to act on their recognition of the hazards of smoking. And a ban which goes unenforced, or is partially enforced, will surely contribute to scofflawry, and hence might do more harm than good.

The prohibition of smoking in designated places is another kind of control already in widespread use — either as a fire prevention measure, or for the comfort of non-smokers, or for other reasons. Thus no one smokes in church or chapel; many courtrooms, theatres, buses, elevators, and libraries prohibit smoking; and there are non-smoking sections in railroad cars, waiting rooms, and other public places.

The current realization of the public health hazards of smoking has led to suggestions that the number and kinds of places where smoking is prohibited be expanded and that existing rules be enforced. In several English cities, including even London — dubbed "the most smoke-easy city" in the world — officials are reported to be considering a ban on smoking in theaters and places of amusement. Hospitals, clinics, and doctors' and dentists' offices are other possible candidates for the list of places where smoking might be made taboo. Poland has some non-smoking cafés and restaurants.

There are weighty arguments both in favor of and against such limited local prohibitions. One major argument in favor concerns the need for constant reminders of the public health hazards of smoking. We are at present, hour after hour all day long, being reminded repeatedly of the pleasurable lure of cigarettes by the advertisements, by the display of cigarettes for sale at every turn, by the ubiquitous presence of ashtrays, and above all by the people smoking around us.

A gradually expanding network of places where smoking is forbidden might similarly serve to remind us, hour by hour and day by day, that smoking is not always and everywhere acceptable. Spitting was once socially acceptable and spittoons were found even in fashionable parlors. Legal bans against spitting in public places helped bring spitting into social disfavor in private places as well. "Wider restriction of smoking in public places," says the Royal College of Physicians report, ". . . might ultimately contribute much to the discontinuance of smoking by altering social acceptance of the habit."

DENMARK *("Smoking is dangerous . . . better not do it")*

CHAPTER 18
Taxation

TODAY cigarettes are inexpensive enough in the United States so that most middle-income adults, and perhaps many with less than a median income, can afford to light up and light up again without thinking about the cost on each occasion. Consumption might be curtailed, it is argued, if each package purchased or even each cigarette lit represented an expense large enough to be pondered.

On at least one historic occasion, taxation did help to curb a public health hazard. During the early 18th century, England was becoming a dropsy-ridden nation as a result of gin priced so cheaply that even beggars could get drunk and stay drunk. The etchings of Hogarth portray the social dissolution which followed. The Royal College of Physicians in 1725 called the Government's attention to the disastrous consequences, and a heavy tax on gin was thereupon levied. Drinking ceased to be a daily preoccupation and became a luxury indulged in occasionally.

That was the first venture of the Royal College of Physicians into the field of public health recommendations; its latest report on smoking suggests that taxation be similarly used to discourage cigarette smoking today.

At first sight, it might appear that cigarettes are already taxed heavily in the United States. Here are the average figures, derived from U. S. Department of Agriculture and Tobacco Tax Council statistics for 1961:

Cost per pack before taxes	14¢
Federal tax	8
Average state tax	5
Retail price	27¢

Cigarette taxes thus take 48 per cent of the American consumer's cigarette outlay.

The Tobacco Tax Council, an industry organization, points out that taxes amount to "four times as much as growers receive" for the tobacco in a pack of cigarettes, and declares, "No other product in America, so widely used by the nation's citizens, bears a burden so oppressive."

As compared with other countries, however, U. S. cigarette taxes are startlingly low. In Great Britain cigarette taxes take 43.2¢ out of the average retail price of 54.7¢ for 20 cigarettes (79%). In Denmark cigarette taxes take 44.8¢ out of the average 56¢ price (80%). In Sweden they take 44¢ out of 52.8¢ (83%). An 80 per cent tax in the United States would amount to 56¢ a pack and raise the average retail price to 70¢ a pack.

Despite the 80 per cent tax already levied on cigarettes in Denmark, the Danish Cancer Society proposed in 1962 that the tax be raised even higher to curtail cigarette consumption.

There are both ethical and practical objections to a general increase in cigarette taxes. The ethical objection arises out of the fact that a cigarette tax, like any other sales or excise tax, bears most heavily upon precisely those persons least able to pay. It is, thus, an inequitable and regressive form of taxation. For example, a 56¢-a-package tax might mean relatively little to a well-to-do American bachelor, but it could constitute a real hardship for a cigarette-addicted, low-income family.

On the practical side, there is little reason to believe that raising the price of cigarettes through taxation (or otherwise) would by itself curtail consumption very much. Economists consider cigarette consumption relatively "inelastic" in relation to price; that is, it neither increases notably when prices fall nor drops off significantly when prices rise. Britons continue to smoke heavily at 54.7¢ for 20 cigarettes.

Moreover, as governments become increasingly dependent on cigarette tax revenues, they tend to develop a built-in interest in the continuation of cigarette smoking, and may even (as in Greece) encourage it. Thus the *Manchester Guardian* quoted a British Chancellor of the Exchequer as saying several years ago, "We at the Treasury don't want too many people to give up smoking." His attitude is understandable. Tobacco excise taxes bring the British Treasury nearly £900 million a year (about $2.5 billion). This is more than the cost of the National Health Service and just less than half of the British defense budget. When taxes reach this level of significance, the government and the tobacco industry are in effect partners.

Even more serious, perhaps, are the adverse *health* effects which might result from increased cigarette prices caused by higher tobacco taxes. British cigarette prices, as we have seen, are already much higher than prices in the United States; and, no doubt in part as a result, British smokers smoke their cigarettes down much closer to the butt end. Raising the cost of cigarettes here would probably tempt at least some American smokers to get more smoke out of each individual cigarette. And as noted in Part I of this book, it is those last drags near the butt end which do the most damage.

Can taxation, then, play any proper role in a campaign to limit smoking?

Selective taxation might be one useful measure. Today in the United States each pack of 20 cigarettes carries the same tax, regardless of cigarette length, or of nicotine and tar content. A more rational approach would be to tax cigarettes in proportion to the nicotine and tar released in their smoke when they are smoked to a designated butt length. A standard method of testing for nicotine and tar content would be needed, of course. This same method could also be used in the regulation of cigarette labeling and advertising, to be discussed next.

Taxing on this basis could contribute its mite to discourage the smoking — and the manufacturing — of high-nicotine and high-tar cigarettes by placing such cigarettes at a competitive price disadvantage.

On the matter of taxation, as at other points in an all-out anti-smoking campaign, judicious timing could prove to be the most effective weapon. Raising prices by raising taxes, while perhaps unwarranted today, might well be worth trying as part of a mop-up campaign after progress had been made on other fronts.

CHAPTER 19
Labeling

ONE IMPORTANT STEP forward in public health generally in recent decades has been the gradual expansion of legal requirements that hazardous products be labeled as such, with appropriate warning notices. The Food and Drug Administration has specified powers to enforce labeling requirements with respect to foods and drugs, and some powers with respect to cosmetics. Its jurisdiction, moreover, has recently been expanded to cover warning labels on household substances. It is the logical agency to exercise jurisdiction over labeling of tobacco products. Some lawyers believe that it has this power already; but to clear up doubts, and to spur the FDA to action, legislation may be needed.

Labeling legislation has from time to time been introduced. In 1957, for example, Senator Wallace F. Bennett of Utah filed a bill in Congress requiring that the following warning be printed on every cigarette package:

> *"Prolonged use of this product may result in cancer, in lung, heart, and circulatory ailments, and in other diseases."*

This bill was referred to the Senate Commerce Committee where, in Senator Bennett's words, "It dropped into a hole, as I knew it would."

184

Similar bills have also been introduced into state legislatures. One filed in the New York State Senate in 1963 would require a label notice on all cigarette packages:

"WARNING — excessive use is dangerous to health."

A labeling bill actually passed the New Mexico Senate but was defeated in the House. It would have required this notice on each package:

"WARNING. This product is habit-forming and is harmful to health."

The Illinois Division of the American Cancer Society and one of the Nebraska medical societies have urged labeling bills on their state legislatures.

Cigarette labels might also be required to reveal the amount of nicotine and tars contained in the smoke. A bill requiring this kind of information on labels was introduced in Congress back in 1955 by Representative Paul A. Fino of New York, and was reintroduced in 1962 and 1963. These bills were referred to the House Interstate and Foreign Commerce Committee; nothing more has been heard of them. A similar bill introduced in 1960 by Representative John A. Blatnik of Minnesota met the same fate.

One problem with nicotine and tar content statements on labels is that the amounts change from time to time as cigarette makers change their tobaccos, processing procedures, or filters. Indeed, two seemingly identical cigarettes on sale at the same time may show a wide variation if made from different batches of tobacco or at different factories. Labeling regulations might therefore also specify (1) that cigarettes differing significantly in nicotine and tar content should not be packaged identically, and (2) that purchasers should be alerted to any changes in content by suitable and conspicuous notices on the label.

To make labels easier to read and interpret, cigarette brands might also be classified into high-content, moderate-content, and low-content groups, and symbols devised which would indicate at a glance to which class a brand belonged.

Legislation has also been proposed requiring a disclosure of how much nicotine and tar each filter actually removes, and forbidding the use of the term "filter" for any device which does not eliminate a stated proportion of the tars and nicotine. The essential health point, however, is not the efficiency of the filter but the amount of nicotine and tar left after filtration. Hence a statement of smoke ingredients is more useful from the health point of view than a statement of filter efficiency.

Labeling requirements, of course, would not by themselves cause smokers to stop smoking. Nor, by themselves, would they deter young people from starting. But as part of a network of reminders, they might contribute to the total effectiveness of any over-all campaign to meet the health problems posed by smoking.

New national labeling legislation, like other proposals for Congressional action on cigarettes, would not be easy to enact. Congress has rarely put through anti-industry measures in the past and, in the normal course of events, is unlikely to do so in the near future. In addition to its own employees and stockholders, the cigarette industry has as potential political allies the farmers who grow the tobacco and the many cigar store owners, newsstand proprietors, and others who sell cigarettes at retail — plus the radio, television, newspaper, magazine, and advertising agency interests which depend in part on cigarette advertising.

It is worth recalling the landmark filter-tip investigation conducted in 1957 by a House Subcommittee under the chairmanship of Representative John A. Blatnik of Minnesota. The committee report charged that cigarette makers had "deceived" the public and that the FTC had "failed in its statutory duty

. . . to approach the problems of false and misleading advertising with vigor and diligence." A year later, Congressman Blatnik told an interviewer, his subcommittee was "reorganized out of business."

D. S. Greenberg later wrote in *Science,* ". . . the incident has passed into the folklore of Congress as a warning that the cigarette industry has potent powers of self-defense. Since Blatnik's investigation, no Congressional committee has gone near the subject."

Nevertheless, there is one political power which can counteract the power of the cigarette industry and its friends. This is the latent power of the voters concerned with public health — which, after all, is their health and their children's. Witness the local and national impact on pesticide controls achieved by public opinion following publication of Rachel Carson's "Silent Spring."

Prompt national action on labeling, moreover, could prove advantageous to the cigarette companies as well as to public health. For packaging chaos would reign if the 50 state legislatures, in the absence of national standards, should erect a crazy-quilt pattern of inconsistent and even conflicting state labeling requirements. To prevent this, a far-sighted industry might accept or even support a sound national cigarette-labeling law.

CHAPTER 20
Regulation of Advertising

THE MOST DIRECT approach to the problem of cigarette advertising, of course, would be to ban it altogether. Strange as it may seem to Americans, one country has actually taken that step.

In Italy all advertising of tobacco products was banned by law on May 16, 1962. The ban covers advertising via newspapers, magazines, radio, television, motion picture theatres, neon signs, posters, and billboards. Offenders guilty of advertising cigarettes are subject to fines ranging up to $3200. Legislators sponsoring the law pointed to the "immorality" of permitting the advertising of products considered harmful to health.

However, in Italy tobacco is a government monopoly. Thus, there was less commercial opposition to the ban than would arise if such a law were under serious consideration in the United States.

Further, Italy imports much of its cigarette supply. In addition to health considerations, the government was no doubt concerned with saving foreign exchange by importing fewer cigarettes. It has even been alleged that the new law was intended to place imported cigarettes (which were widely advertised before the ban) on a more nearly equal competitive footing with domestic cigarettes (which were not advertised).

But regardless of such economic motives, the effect of the Italian action was to terminate all cigarette advertising in that country.

In Finland, advertising of cigarettes on television was ended in July 1962. No law was required; the Finnish TV system is government-owned, and authorities simply decided not to carry any more cigarette advertising. Cigarette companies, which are privately owned, are said to have accepted the decision. The present ban is effective only until the end of 1963; whether it will be renewed thereafter had not been decided at the time of writing.

In Great Britain questions have been asked about cigarette advertising in the House of Commons, and a few actions, both official and voluntary, have been taken.

In April 1962, one month after the Royal College of Physicians' report on smoking and health made a national sensation, and at a time when anti-cigarette feeling was running high, the British cigarette industry announced "voluntarily" that it would no longer advertise cigarettes on British commercial television stations before 9 P.M. Previously, the major British companies had placed about half of their cigarette commercials during the hours from 7 to 9 P.M., when the audience of young people was no doubt very large. In the U.S., an estimated 60 per cent of radio and TV cigarette commercials are aired before 9 P.M.

Also in 1962, Britain's Independent Television Authority, a government agency which regulates commercial television there, announced a change in official advertising standards to avoid "those aspects of advertising which could reasonably be taken to make a special appeal to young people." The cigarette companies thereupon voluntarily extended this ban on "any special appeal to young people" to cover their newspaper advertising and billboards as well.

189

But as with other efforts to regulate advertising *themes*, problems have arisen. A typical cigarette advertisement in England before the ban, as in the United States today, might have showed a handsome young man and an attractive girl sitting side by side, looking fondly and healthfully at one another while their two cigarettes smoldered together in an ashtray. The new British rule against youth appeals blots out the young man and the girl, but the gain is small. "Nowadays," a British trade paper reports, "*Players* ads show two cigarettes smoking in an ashtray. The smokers are not to be seen. What they are doing is left to the imagination."

In New Zealand the Department of Health has been concerned with this problem of glamorous cigarette advertising aimed at young people, and has asked major tobacco companies to follow the British lead voluntarily. The companies are said to have agreed, but to have requested time to make necessary arrangements. Also, the New Zealand Broadcasting Corporation (a government body) has restricted the content of cigarette commercials on radio and television. The industry responded with a reprisal; it withdrew all advertising from these media. Thus the practical effect of a seemingly mild regulation was to bring about at least a temporary end to all radio and TV cigarette commercials in the country.

In the United States, of course, cigarette companies have long been legally subject to the same restrictions as other advertisers with respect to "false and misleading" claims. The sorry tale of the Federal Trade Commission's efforts to enforce such restrictions has been told in Part III of this book.

A cigarette company presumably advertises for two quite distinct reasons: first, to attract smokers who are currently smoking other brands; and second, to attract non-smokers — especially youthful non-smokers, who may continue to smoke the product for many years or decades to come. The chief public health concern, obviously, is with advertising likely to attract youthful non-smokers to the smoking habit. The extensive cigarette advertisements run in college newspapers are, as we have seen, a clear example of such recruiting tactics. Some college newspapers have already discontinued cigarette advertisements, and a similar policy is under consideration on a number of other campuses. A California legislator has introduced a bill in the state legislature banning tobacco advertising from all school and college newspapers in the state.

The distribution of free cigarette samples on college campuses and at other places where young people congregate is a form of advertising particularly objectionable from the public health point of view. A few colleges have already taken action to discourage this practice, too; others might well follow suit, or state laws against free distribution might be considered.

Several state legislatures have considered laws regulating cigarette advertising. A Minnesota bill, for example, would have forbidden ads showing people smoking. If passed, it would have posed questions in connection with such advertising originating outside Minnesota but circulating within it. Similarly, a range of widely differing state cigarette advertising laws might present other problems to cigarette advertisers. Again, as with labeling laws, national legislation would have the virtue of being uniform, letting the advertiser know where he stood in all 50 states.

A few national publications (notably *Reader's Digest*) refuse cigarette advertisements; and former Governor LeRoy Collins urging that radio and television stations refuse cigarette commercials aimed at young people has already been mentioned. "This is something that goes to the basic health of the young people of our nation," Mr. Collins told an interviewer. "It has to do not with veracity or the technical quality of advertising, but the substance and purpose." Referring to the exploitation in cigarette advertisements of sports figures popular among young people, Mr. Collins remarked, "The cigarette people say their advertising isn't specially geared to youth. But a grown person doesn't care what brand Roger Maris smokes."

One possible solution might follow the lines of an agreement voluntarily worked out by Danish tobacco companies, all of which agreed no longer to solicit cigarette testimonials from athletic heroes. They reached a further agreement among themselves restricting cigarette advertising solely to newspapers, a communications medium primarily for adults. In West Germany some cigarette manufacturers have discontinued billboard advertising. As of this writing, two New York advertising agencies have reportedly adopted a policy that they will neither solicit nor accept a cigarette account. The president of one of the agencies was quoted as saying, "I smoke myself, but I don't want to be responsible for converting others to the habit."

Research would no doubt prove helpful in further decisions about cigarette advertising. A survey might be made of present cigarette advertising, for example, to determine which advertising media are actually being used to recruit new smokers, and what themes are being stressed for this purpose. Simultaneously, a survey of children and young people might be made to gauge the impact of cigarette advertising.

There are ways in which the impact of cigarette advertising might be lessened on adult smokers as well. For one thing, the FTC might coordinate its advertising regulatory powers with the FDA's labeling controls to the end that tar and nicotine content might be meaningfully analyzed and then reinstated in cigarette advertising. And the Federal Communications Commission might rule on whether radio and TV licensees that carry cigarette commercials are indeed acting in the public interest, as they are required to do.

CHAPTER 21

Help for the Smoker

SOME SMOKERS (including men and women who have smoked a pack or two a day for many years) can stop smoking without difficulty, or with only temporary discomfort, by an act of will. Dr. Daniel Horn, Assistant Chief for Program Research of the Public Health Service Cancer Control Program, is an example. "I simply put away my cigarettes one fine October day," he reports, "after running some cards through an IBM machine."

On the other hand, the world is full of smokers who are sincerely convinced that they should stop and are eager to do so, but who — like Sigmund Freud (see page 91) — find they cannot. Some of these smokers-in-spite-of-themselves, moreover, have cardiovascular conditions, gastric ulcers, or precancerous lesions which may make abstaining quite literally a matter of life or death. There is an important health interest to be served in making available to those unwilling smokers the most effective medical and psychological assistance that scientific research can devise.

One hopeful "smoke-weaning" technique has been developed by Dr. Börje Ejrup, associate professor of medicine at Stockholm's famed Karolinska Institute, and has been used with more than 6000 patients at six Swedish clinics since 1956. His tobacco withdrawal clinics, Dr. Ejrup explains, are designed to fill the gap between the doctor's order, "You have to stop smoking," and the patient's answer, "Yes, I would like to, but how?"

The treatment consists of individual discussions between doctor and patient; daily injections of nicotine or nicotine-like substances in an effort to assuage the craving for tobacco smoke; plus, in some cases, tranquilizers, appetite-suppressing drugs, or other medications. One of the drugs used makes the smoke distasteful to some patients. Dr. Ejrup also distributes to his clinic patients a handbook on how to stop.

Dr. Ejrup reports good results from this combination of indoctrination, personal consultation with a physician, and medication. By the tenth day of treatment, three-fourths of one group of patients had stopped smoking entirely. Six months later, half of those who had stopped stated in response to a questionnaire that they were continuing to benefit. They were either not smoking at all, or smoking fewer cigarettes, or smoking cigars or pipes. The Ejrup clinic has now expanded its schedule to include periodical follow-up visits from patients to supplement the initial ten-day series of consultations and treatments. (Originally priced at $15 for a ten-day treatment, the cost was later raised to $30.)

Some questions remain concerning Dr. Ejrup's success. For example, it has been suggested that a six-month follow-up period is not long enough for an evaluation of the procedures; Freud, after all, stopped smoking for 14 months only to start again. Also, Dr. Ejrup personally saw and worked with the patients; whether others with different personalities would have equal success with his methods remains to be determined. These and other questions may be answered in due course; an American clinic under Dr. Ejrup's supervision was scheduled to open during 1963 in New York.

Half a dozen clinics modeled after the Swedish forerunners

have also been launched in England, some private and some sponsored by local health authorities. The drugs used are made available without charge by the National Health Service. England also has a National Society of Non-Smokers, patterned after Alcoholics Anonymous, which offers weekend or longer courses in how to stop smoking.

Similar programs are springing up in the United States, some commercial and some non-profit. There are also some so-called "guidance centers" which are not really clinics at all but retail outlets for anti-smoking products.

Proving the success of a how-to-stop-smoking procedure is very difficult, but failures are easy to spot. In one American experiment, for example, 17 smokers who wished to stop took part in a series of group therapy sessions under a qualified clinical psychologist. After nine meetings in six weeks, 12 of the 17 were not smoking. After three months, eight were still abstaining. But after 18 months, 14 of the original 17 were either still smoking or smoking again.

Clearly there is need for far more intensive research on this problem, and need for funds to finance such research. The U.S. Public Health Service and National Institutes of Health might appropriately meet this need, along with such voluntary agencies as the American Cancer Society, the American Heart Association, and the National Tuberculosis Association. Perhaps what is needed is a School for Tobacco Studies similar to the one for alcohol studies formerly at Yale and now at Rutgers.

For a discussion of how to lessen the risk if you can't stop smoking, see Part I, page 91. For a discussion of some products marketed to help smokers stop smoking, see Appendix A, page 212. Advice on *how to stop smoking is available in one section of an English book entitled, "Common Sense about Smoking," by C. M. Fletcher and others, distributed in the United States at 65¢ by Penguin Books, Inc., 3300 Clipper Mill Road, Baltimore 11, Maryland.*

CHAPTER 22
Public Education

NONE OF THE PROPOSALS we have been considering — prohibitions, taxation, labeling, regulation of advertising, and therapeutic help for those who already want to stop smoking — really reaches to the heart of the matter. For ultimately the decision to smoke or not to smoke is made personally by each man, woman, and child. Most public health leaders and organizations, accordingly, place their initial and greatest emphasis on measures designed to affect individual attitudes toward smoking. Such educational measures, it is hoped, may win support even from smokers who don't want to stop smoking themselves, or who want to but can't.

The British have organized various programs with such ends in view. Following publication of the momentous Royal College of Physicians report in 1962, for example, British health authorities distributed 820,000 anti-smoking posters. Ten poster designs were included, each bearing the official imprint of the Ministry of Health. Some carried a blunt, straightforward text:
> *"DANGER. The more cigarettes you smoke,*
> *the greater the risk of death from lung*
> *cancer, chronic bronchitis or*
> *heart disease. You have been warned."*

Others offered more subtle appeals, and were illustrated. Several of these posters, along with similar posters from other countries, are reproduced on the accompanying pages of this book.

The Ministry of Health also dispatched three panel trucks with two-man crews to tour England with lectures, literature, posters, and other visual-aid materials; these units visited the areas least accessible to regular health officials. A similar mobile unit was equipped to carry the facts to schools throughout London.

Other British government departments joined the Ministry of Health in such efforts. The Admiralty warned sailors of the dangers of smoking. The Minister of Education alerted all teachers, urging a "fresh, positive approach" to discourage youth from smoking. September 1963 was set as the target date for beginning a massive program directed at school children.

The immediate practical effect of the poster campaign and other efforts touched off by the Royal College of Physicians report was striking. Retail tobacco sales dropped 20 per cent. But then they began to rise again. It is still too early to judge the long-range effects.

Denmark, too, has stressed educational measures. Radio Denmark has been carrying broadcasts on smoking and lung cancer since 1956. A nationwide anti-smoking campaign aimed at youth was launched in 1961, using brochures, posters, and films. The Danes believe in starting early; one booklet went to every school child above the third grade. And positive efforts are made to explain to the children the fact that men and women who smoke do not necessarily want to smoke or approve smoking. "These lines are not written by a fanatic and diehard boy scout leader," one booklet explains. " . . . They are written by a heavy smoker — by a man who smokes about 50 cigarettes a day — but who earnestly wishes he had just never lighted the first one."

A poster contest for Danish school children drew 6500 entries and provided many leads to the way children themselves feel about smoking. Copies of the winning posters were sent to many schools where other children could see them. Pamphlets were distributed containing anti-cigarette testimonials from leading sports figures, and featuring photographs of merchandise attractive to children which could be purchased with money not spent on cigarettes. Moderate success was reported from the use of these methods.

In the United States the American Cancer Society has taken the lead in similar measures. It has been distributing information on smoking and health since 1954. More than 3,500,000 copies of one Society pamphlet, "To Smoke or Not to Smoke," have been distributed. This pamphlet also forms the nucleus of a classroom kit, including filmstrip and phonograph records, and a well-received film ("Is Smoking Worth It?"), which has been circulated to 25,000 secondary schools in which an estimated half of the country's high school students are enrolled. In 1963 an educational program addressed to sixth, seventh, and eighth-graders was added. Cancer Society studies, reports, and releases have had enormous circulation through newspapers and some magazines, and through occasional radio and television programs. The Society's local chapters have also been active in public health education in their own communities.

In some programs the American Heart Association, National Tuberculosis Association, and American Public Health Association have worked with the Society. An example is the quarterly *Medical Bulletin on Tobacco*, sponsored jointly by the four associations and distributed to 200,000 physicians.

A major contribution of the Society has been to explore and evaluate alternative themes to be stressed in educational programs. It has sponsored youth conferences, for example, at which outstanding young people have been brought together to discuss the cigarette-cancer problem and to recommend educational methods likely to prove effective among their classmates.

The outstanding Cancer Society effort of this kind was an eight-month study of 22,000 high school boys and girls in Portland, Oregon, initiated by Dr. Daniel Horn in 1958.

This Horn study first of all determined actual smoking habits. It revealed that 14.5 per cent of Portland freshman boys and 4.6 per cent of freshman girls were already smoking. The proportions increased each year until among seniors 35.4 per cent of the boys and 26.2 per cent of the girls were smokers. Dr. Horn calculated that "10 per cent of those who are going to become smokers develop the habit with some degree of regularity *before* the teens — about 65 per cent develop it during their high school years."

The Portland students were next divided into six groups. One group served as a control and received no smoking instruction or educational materials. The other five were exposed to five different educational approaches:

CONTEMPORARY: emphasizing aspects of smoking immediately applicable to high school students, such as expense, relation to athletic performance, attractiveness to the opposite sex.

REMOTE: stressing physical effects such as lung cancer likely to show up in later life.

AUTHORITATIVE: providing admonitory health messages with a flat laying down of rules.

BOTH-SIDED: taking a permissive attitude; conceding that smoking is socially acceptable; dealing broadmindedly with the pros and cons alike; leaving the final decision to the students.

ADULT ROLE-TAKING: having the students reverse the usual parent-child roles and providing information on smoking and health to their parents and other adult relatives.

A follow-up study established the significant fact that any of these approaches was better than none. All five groups ex-

199

posed to the educational programs yielded fewer recruits to smoking than did the control group.

The most effective approach was the "remote" approach, stressing lung cancer and other late effects of smoking. The "contemporary" approach was about as effective with girls, but not with boys. The "both-sided" approach was fairly effective; "authoritative" and "role-taking" approaches were less so.

"Essentially," Dr. Horn explained, "the theme of the most successful approach was the one emphasizing the eventual effects and may be paraphrased as follows: 'You've heard a lot of arguments about smoking cigarettes, but there is something new to be said on the subject. Scientists have recently found out that the smoking of cigarettes can cause lung cancer. This is something that was not formerly known; now there is not much doubt. Here is some of the evidence. . . . Think before you decide whether or not you ought to smoke.'"

As a result of the Portland program, only five per cent — instead of the usual 10 per cent — of the non-smoking students became smokers during the school year. "Carried on cumulatively," Dr. Horn remarked, "for a period of four years it would mean that about 20 per cent of our high school students who would otherwise become regular smokers by graduation time would not do so; in other words, the percentage of smokers could be cut in half."

The Horn study represents an important pioneering effort in a much-neglected research area. But it is only a bare beginning. A whole roster of other urgently needed studies might easily be drawn up, covering all ages from nursery school to the elderly, determining present attitudes toward smoking and gauging the effects of programs designed to affect these attitudes. In this, as in other respects, the resources currently available fall far short of the need.

In all of its activities, the Cancer Society makes it plain

that its objections to smoking are *medical* — not moral, religious, or social. The American Temperance Society, in contrast, takes a specifically moral stand against smoking, and makes frank use of the "scare approach" avoided by most public health groups. Its motion picture shows in vivid, bloody detail an operation for lung cancer, with a close-up of a cancer-riddled lung being lifted out of the patient's chest cavity.

There is, of course, no need to look for and adopt any single educational approach; persons who might be untouched by one may well be convinced by another.

To date, no national organization concerned solely with the cigarette problem has sprung up, but a few local groups have been established. One is the Cigarette Cancer Committee at Roswell Park Memorial Institute, a leading cancer research institute in Buffalo, New York. Formed in 1962, the CCC has held seminars on smoking and health for Buffalo-area teachers. It has supplied speakers for local meetings and local TV programs. It has publicized the results of cigarette research projects. And it has shown a modest flair for bringing the light touch to advertising against cigarettes.

The Committee distributes books of matches, for example, with a small ruler on the edge so that smokers can measure the length of their butts — a cogent reminder that the shorter the butt the heavier the load of nicotine and tars inhaled. "Measure your smoke for safety" is the legend. A poster showing a sylvan scene notably free of smoke bears the caption, "Why filter springtime?" Other posters and match books poke gentle fun at smokers while providing health information.

The CCC successfully arranged for the removal of cigarette vending machines from the Institute and posted notices where the machines had stood:

> "Roswell Park Memorial Institute is dedicated to the detection, treatment, and prevention of cancer. To help protect and remind you of

the hazards of cigarette smoking, all cigarette vending machines have been removed from the premises. Research at Roswell Park has proved conclusively that cigarette smoking is a major cause of lung cancer. It also increases diseases of the heart and blood vessels, chronic bronchitis, and gastro-intestinal disorders."

Finally, the Committee has been active in urging such legislative actions as a higher state tax on cigarettes and a cigarette-labeling law.

In several respects the Buffalo group resembles local organizations of scientists established earlier to supply educational leadership with respect to radiation hazards, including nuclear fallout. Originating in St. Louis and New York, these radiation groups soon spread to other leading scientific centers; recently the local groups banded together to form a national organization. It is at least possible that other local Cigarette Cancer Committees or their equivalents may be formed and may eventually coalesce into a national information and action organization.

An increasing number of American colleges, too, are becoming active in the public health campaign against cigarette smoking. At the University of Pittsburgh, for example, signs are posted close to each cigarette vending machine:

"Think Before You Smoke. Cigarettes Can Cause Cancer and Other Diseases."

The Student Health Service there includes education on smoking in its general health education program. New York University has prohibited promotional contests run on the campus by cigarette companies. Tufts has banned cigarette ads from its football programs and cigarette commercials from radio and TV broadcasts of college games. Manhattan College has speakers from the American Cancer Society and from its own Student Health Service address the freshman class. Several colleges are reconsidering their rules on smoking in class. These examples are typical of many others. The universities and colleges as a whole, however, have still to adopt comprehensive programs or consistent policies with respect to smoking and the ubiquitous campus promotion of smoking. Nor have university social science and psychology departments as yet contributed much to research on smoking motivation and on effective measures to discourage smoking.

Most public school systems in the United States have for many years included anti-cigarette materials in their curricula, usually as a part of their health education courses. Such material is prescribed in 32 of the 50 states. Much of it, in all probability, needs to be revised in the light of recent medical research and in the light of the findings of the Portland high school study.

One notable effort to update school materials was begun in 1963 in Pennsylvania, where the State Health Department and the State Department of Public Instruction collaborated on an information program aimed at elementary school students *before* they entered high school. A nationwide study of the amount and quality of smoking education efforts in our school systems, followed by recommendations for improvement, is a project American educators could consider.

Adult education, too, is an area where much might be done. Here state health departments, which are currently running education programs on a variety of other health hazards, might well take the lead. Some have already begun. The Oregon Board of Health, for example, passed a resolution in 1963 designating cigarette smoking "harmful"; it also appropriated a modest sum to publicize the effects of smoking on health, and to sponsor a series of state educational conferences.

All of the efforts we have been describing suffer, however, one major handicap. Public health officials and educators are accustomed to take their lead in considerable part from United States government policy as enunciated by the Public Health

Service. The Public Health Service campaign against venereal diseases under Surgeon General Thomas Parran during the 1930s was an early example of this leadership. The Public Health Service program on polio vaccines is a recent example. The absence of a similar nationally coordinated program in the field of cigarette-smoking education makes it much more difficult for state and local agencies, official and voluntary, to act in their respective areas. State and local groups considering action are often faced with the objection, "If this were so important, the government would do something about it."

This gap in the education program may some day be filled, as the next chapter indicates.

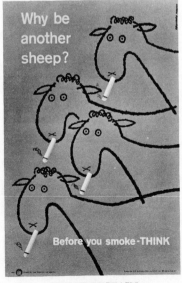

GREAT BRITAIN

CHAPTER 23

A National Health Program

BACK IN JUNE 1961, the American Cancer Society, American Heart Association, American Public Health Association, and National Tuberculosis Association sent a joint letter to President Kennedy urging the establishment of a national commission on smoking and health, similar to commissions he had already established on cancer and on heart disease "to examine the social responsibilities of business, of voluntary agencies, and of government in the education of the youth of America; and to recommend various ways to protect the public." Little happened until May 1962, when the President was asked a question about smoking and health at a press conference. Governmental wheels then started rolling; on June 7, 1962, Surgeon General Luther Terry announced that he would appoint an impartial committee of specialists.

This group, known as the Surgeon General's Advisory Committee on Smoking and Health, is composed of medical specialists not publicly committed on the cigarette-health issue. While it is not the kind of action commission the health agencies requested, it is a step in the right direction. It has a staff of full-time experts and part-time consultants, and has been spending many months on its task of preparing findings. A preliminary report is now expected some time before the end of this year. It is expected that a second group of experts will be empanelled to make concrete recommendations for action based on the findings; but these recommendations are not expected until well along in 1964 at the earliest.

The importance of the findings and recommendations which should emerge eventually can hardly be overestimated. For in addition to the weight they will carry with the public directly, they can also influence the policies of other Federal agencies, and will be looked to for guidance by state and local agencies, official and voluntary. Congress, and the state legislatures, too, may consult the Advisory Committee reports for legislative guidelines.

In the short run, however, the existence of the Surgeon General's Advisory Committee has had a delaying effect on public health education and on official action. Other agencies of the government can and do use the existence of the Advisory Committee as an excuse for doing nothing now. The Federal Trade Commission, for example, under considerable pressure to repeal its ban preventing companies with low-nicotine and low-tar cigarettes from advertising their merits, has staved off the issue by saying that it is waiting for the Advisory Committee to say something.

We cannot, of course, prejudge what the Advisory Committee's findings will be; and the recommendations for action, equally unknown, may be a year or more off. A general position of the kind already adopted by Britain's Royal College of Physicians and many other authoritative bodies is, of course, one possibility. If such a position were taken the opportunities for supplementary Federal actions would be numerous.

The Office of Education, for example, might then be able to design and foster cigarette education programs for schools.

The National Institutes of Health might launch research into smoking motivation, methods to help smokers stop smoking, and related topics; it might also provide grants for such studies at other institutions.

The Public Health Service might establish pilot projects in public health education on cigarette hazards, and make grants-in-aid to the states for similar programs.

The Federal Trade Commission might take effective action to bring cigarette advertising into conformity with fact, and might even apply the doctrine of "affirmative disclosure" to require warning notices in cigarette advertising. And the list could be extended to cover comparable actions by other Federal agencies.

One branch of the government has not waited for the Surgeon General's Advisory Committee to take action. The United States Air Force late in 1962 barred cigarette companies from distributing free cigarettes in Air Force hospitals or flight lunch boxes; and it has introduced materials on the hazards of smoking into its health education program for Air Force personnel.

"It seems inconsistent and contradictory," said an Air Force spokesman, "for us to work diligently for our patients' good health with one hand and distribute harmful agents with the other."

In addition to looking to the United States government for leadership on public health issues, Americans customarily look to the medical profession itself. Some leadership is currently being provided. Studies have shown, for example, that physicians are giving up smoking at a more rapid rate than laymen, and that those who find they can't stop are increasingly switching to cigars or pipes. Five state medical associations (in California, Maine, New York, Pennsylvania, and Utah) have passed anti-cigarette resolutions urging public health education on the question. Some county medical societies have also joined educational efforts — including a few in tobacco-growing states.

To date, the American Medical Association has not spoken

out with a clear voice. When members urged action on the
AMA in June 1962, it announced that it would appoint a committee of impartial experts; subsequently, however, plans for
such a committee were abandoned.

An objective observer, reviewing the progress made to date
in the field of public health education, would be forced to
conclude that not enough has been accomplished to make any
significant dent in national cigarette consumption figures.
Nevertheless, he would be able to discern the gradually emerg-
ing outlines of programs under both governmental and voluntary auspices which *could* make a dent in consumption, and
could in addition affect attitudes toward smoking among those
who continue to smoke.

One resource seriously lacking, however, is money. The
American Cancer Society is probably spending more on smoking education efforts than any other agency, public or private;
but its funds are severely limited. It has less than $8,000,000
to spend on health education — and this must be spread to
cover all kinds of cancer and all ways of preventing, treating,
and curing it, so that relatively little is available for education
about smoking.

Iceland has taken the lead in pioneering a simple, logical
method of financing an effective health program. It has levied
a ½¢-a-pack additional tax on cigarettes, and turns the proceeds (about $50,000) over to the Icelandic Cancer Society
for research and health education.

A similar ½¢-a-pack tax on cigarettes in the United States
would yield roughly $125 million a year — less than is cur-
rently spent on cigarette advertising, but still an impressive
amount. The money could be distributed, as existing health
research and education funds are distributed, for the operations of Federal agencies, for grants-in-aid to the states, and for
grants to appropriate non-governmental organizations.

If opposition to an additional ½¢ tax were to prove strong, an equivalent amount might be earmarked from the existing Federal cigarette tax, reducing the net yield from the present $2 billion-a-year level to just under $1.9 billion. State legislatures might also consider an additional ½¢ tax to finance state cigarette research and education programs.

Even in hard cash terms, the expenditure of substantial sums on cigarette education could be justified. For if the economic costs of smoking are added up — medical care for illnesses resulting from smoking, days lost from work during illness, days lost through premature death, public assistance to families requiring it because of the death of the breadwinner, fires set by cigarettes and matches — $125 million a year seems like a modest sum indeed for a program to curb such losses.

Would such a program be successful?

The results of limited approaches tried to date offer only glimmers of hope. Certainly no one approach taken in isolation can claim much effectiveness.

The same might be said, however, for any one cigarette advertisement. We gradually became a cigarette-smoking nation as a result of constantly repeated, ever-expanding efforts to establish the habit. Some cigarette advertising campaigns failed; others succeeded. As more and more men smoked cigarettes, they became living advertisements for the practice. Anti-cigarette prejudices crumbled, anti-cigarette laws were repealed, and smoking became socially acceptable. Women began to smoke, too, and young people began to smoke at an earlier and earlier age.

All this took time, money, and effort.

Public health educators argue that a similar cumulative effect might gradually convert us into a non-cigarette-smoking nation again. Trial-and-error education programs would have to come first, backed by research to determine what efforts yielded the highest dividends. Each non-smoker would become a living reminder of the reasons for not smoking. Advertising against cigarettes would reinforce such reminders. As attitudes toward smoking changed, moreover, action along the specific lines discussed in the preceding chapters would become possible and advisable. Legal measures, in turn, might then reinforce the effects of the public health education and the special advertising programs.

All this would take time, money and effort, too.

Shall we give the time, spend the money, make the effort? If we don't it will not be for lack of knowledge of the threat or because means of dealing with it are beyond our grasp.

CU's tests of cigarettes over past years have been made with the apparatus shown above. What CU has learned has been that brands vary widely and change frequently with respect to tars and nicotine in the smoke (see pages 217-218)

APPENDIX A
The Anti-Smoking Drugs

A current drug trade product directory lists about three dozen brand names under the heading of "Smoking Deterrents." None of these products, Consumers Union's medical consultants say, has ever been shown convincingly to do more to help a smoker shake his habit than ordinary candy drops or chewing gum taken with equivalent faith.

The formula of a smoking deterrent generally is based on one of three main types of ingredients — topical anesthetics such as benzocaine or menthol (found, for example, in *Ban-Smoke Chewing Gum, Pronicotyl,* Thompson *Nosmoke Chewing Gum*); astringents such as silver nitrate (found in *Fumex*); or lobeline sulfate, a chemical which is very much like nicotine in its effects on the nervous system (found in many brands, including *Bantron* and the new *Nikoban,* which has been aiming a strong and persistent advertising campaign at the nation's physicians).

The rationale for using an anesthetic in a smoking deterrent is obscure, and even the manufacturers seem a bit unsure about it. The *Ban-Smoke* leaflet, for example, hesitantly explains, "It appears that *Ban-Smoke* dulls the yearning of the taste buds for tobacco flavor." No controlled studies have been published to prove that these products do help break the smoking habit. Moreover, topical anesthetics applied to the skin are known to sensitize some people; how often such a reaction might

212

follow repeated application of an anesthetic to the mucous membranes is unknown.

Astringent mouthwashes containing alum, silver nitrate, or other metallic materials that dry or pucker the mouth were promoted many years ago as tobacco-habit breakers, possibly on the theory that they would make the mouth so oversensitive to the irritating properties of tobacco smoke that the act of smoking would lose its enjoyment. These materials were either so unpleasant of themselves or so ineffective that interest in them quickly waned. *Fumex*, however, has revived the idea in recent years in the form of lozenges rather than a mouth-wash. The company's advertising brochure for physicians, which outlines the bases for claims of effectiveness, is far from convincing. The lozenges have not been used by a sufficiently large group of subjects over a sufficiently long period, and there has been no report of a really carefully controlled double-blind study (in which the lozenges and a placebo would be tested against each other with neither the smokers nor the investigators knowing who got what).

The use of lobeline in smoking deterrents is based on the theory that, since lobeline and nicotine have similar actions on the nervous system, one can substitute lobeline for nicotine and then gradually withdraw the lobeline, thus weaning a person from the tobacco habit. The theory sounds reasonable, but the drug (at least when used alone and not as part of an organized therapeutic program) has not been proved effective from the long-range point of view; nor is it free from undesirable side-effects. Such symptoms as faintness, vomiting, stomach pain, and loss of appetite are fairly common.

In 1955, Drs. G. W. Rapp and A. A. Olin of Chicago reported[1] that they could control the stomach side-effects by combining lobeline with a small amount of an antacid. They tested this combination (the formula of *Bantron*) on smokers, and reported that "More than 80% of the chronic smokers gave up smoking entirely *without undue effort* after taking the pills for five or six days." But their test report did not indicate how long these changed smoking habits may have lasted.

Several years later, Dr. Rapp, working with two other researchers in a project paid for in part by the makers of *Bantron*, pitted *Bantron* against unbuffered lobeline sulfate and measured blood levels of lobeline. They reported[2] that *Bantron* gave much higher levels than lobeline sulfate alone. At the same time they reported that *Bantron* reduced from 17.8 to 14.6 the number of cigarettes smoked per day by smokers who wanted to quit, while placebos had negligible effect.

These are the tests on which claims for the lobeline products are based. But they are in remarkable contrast with careful tests done elsewhere.

A team of British investigators, Drs. R. A. Miley and W. G. White, for example, have reported[3] tests with three types of tablets made to look alike. One contained lobeline and an antacid, plus a small amount of copper sulfate in a sugar coating; the second type contained an antacid and copper sulfate, but no lobeline; the third type was a placebo, containing antacid only. Copper sulfate, like the silver nitrate in *Fumex* lozenges, is an astringent, and each pill was to be retained in the mouth for a few seconds to allow it to work.

---

[1]*American Journal of Medical Sciences, 230:9, 1955.*
[2]*American Journal of Medical Sciences, 237:287, 1959.*
[3]*British Medical Journal, 1:101, 1958.*

In all, 60 volunteers anxious to give up smoking took part in the experiment. Approximately 25 per cent of each group succeeded in stopping completely or reducing drastically their daily cigarette consumption, *regardless of the type of tablet they were taking.* A little over 50 per cent of the volunteer testers were smoking fewer cigarettes towards the end of the second week than when they first started, again *regardless of the type of tablet they were taking.* Less than 25 per cent of the panel failed to respond at all. The obvious conclusion is that the wish to see the tobacco habit broken may be a more powerful deterrent than the type of chemical employed.

An equally interesting test has been reported[4] by W. A. Bartlett and Dr. R. W. Whitehead of Denver, Colo. Their subjects, who had smoked for many years and wished to quit, were divided into three groups. One group took *Bantron;* a second group took apparently similar tablets containing a tranquilizer; and the third group took sugar pills. Again there were no significant differences in the results obtained.

APPENDIX B
Little Cigars vs. Cigarettes

Cigarette smokers trying to ease over gently to a safer smoke may think of taking up little cigars — those products which match cigarettes in size and shape and differ from cigarettes,

---

[4]*Journal of Laboratory and Clinical Medicine*, 50:278, 1957.

to the eye, only in that their wrappers are made of tobacco rather than paper. But this switch poses problems, as tests run by Consumers Union several years ago showed. Twelve brands of little cigars and eight brands of 5¢ cigars were tested for tar and nicotine content, and the little cigars were submitted to a panel of smokers, some of whom regularly smoked cigarettes and some of whom smoked regular-size cigars.

The composite results of the tar and nicotine tests, along with results of tests on 39 brands of cigarettes, were as follows:

	TARS		NICOTINE	
	Av. mg.*	Av. mg. per puff	Av. mg.*	Av. mg. per puff
LITTLE CIGARS — 12 brands	53	4.7	3.2	0.28
CIGARETTES — 39 brands+	36	3.5	2.0	0.19
5¢ CIGARS — 8 brands	62	2.0	5.1	0.16

*Little cigars and cigarettes were smoked to a 25mm butt, 5¢ cigars to a 40mm butt.

With reference to these figures, CU's medical adviser pointed out that "switching from cigarettes to little cigars will not reduce the hazard if the smoker still inhales. In fact, if the same number of little cigars as cigarettes is smoked and inhaled, the adverse effects on the lungs, circulatory system, and other organs may be much greater, since the smoke of little cigars contains more nicotine and tars than an equivalent amount of cigarette smoke."

In the panel test, the cigarette smokers inhaled the little-cigar smoke just as they inhaled cigarette smoke. Only those smokers who tried the brands judged strongest said that continued use of these smokes might lead them to give up inhaling. But the brands judged strongest by the panel, interestingly enough, were not those found highest in nicotine and tars in the laboratory tests. Four brands, the highest of all in tars, were judged by the panel to be mildest and most like cigarettes. The reason for this apparent discrepancy, laboratory tests showed, was that the smoke of the four "mild" brands was less alkaline than that of the other eight brands. The irritating effect of high alkalinity has been suggested as the reason why cigar smoke is rarely inhaled.

Thus, in CU's tests, the brands of little cigars most likely to appeal to cigarette smokers were those least likely to discourage inhaling, which were the very brands offering the greatest threat from tars and nicotine.

APPENDIX C
Cigarettes by Types

Consumers Union tested and reported on the tar and nicotine yields of U.S. and Canadian cigarettes several times during the period when king-size and filter-tip models were burgeoning and the Tar Derby was in full swing. A summary of the findings is presented below (30 to 45 U.S. brands were covered in each test project and 8 to 18 Canadian). During this period, as evidence linking cigarettes and disease mounted, there was a noticeable downward trend of tar and nicotine yields for all types of cigarettes.

Tests on individual brands showed that many filter cigarettes yielded less than half as much tar and nicotine as some unfiltered brands, although, to be sure, a few filter models yielded as much. The *average* yield of the filter cigarettes tested was about two-thirds as high as the yield of the unfiltered. In the 1961 tests, published in the April 1961 issue of CONSUMER REPORTS, the cigarettes lowest in tar and nicotine were three king-size filter models.

CU's findings were obtained by tests (see page 211) in which all cigarettes were smoked to the same butt length. Since the last few puffs are the most heavily loaded, however, a smoker can appreciably reduce his tar and nicotine intake from *any* cigarette by leaving a king-size butt (provided, of course, he does not increase the number of cigarettes he smokes each day).

COMPOSITE OF FINDINGS
Average Tars in Smoke Per Cigarette, in Milligrams

	April 1961	Jan. 1960	Dec. 1958	March 1957	Feb. 1955
Regular size, filter-tip	20	21	27	35	26
Long size, filter-tip	23	25	36	41	–
King size, filter-tip	26	27	35	40	37
Regular size, no filter	30	34	36	41	44
King size, no filter	38	45	46	50	55
AVERAGE OF ALL BRANDS TESTED	27	29	36	42	44

Average Nicotine in Smoke Per Cigarette, in Milligrams

	April 1961	Jan. 1960	Dec. 1958	March 1957	Feb. 1955
Regular size, filter-tip	1.1	1.1	1.6	2.7	1.8
Long size, filter-tip	1.2	1.3	1.9	3.1	–
King size, filter-tip	1.3	1.4	1.9	2.8	2.6
Regular size, no filter	1.7	1.9	2.1	2.7	2.9
King size, no filter	2.1	2.5	2.7	3.2	3.4
AVERAGE OF ALL BRANDS TESTED	1.5	1.5	2.0	2.9	2.8

INDEX

219

Index

Index

DATE DUE

Nov. 24, 63	APR 19 1988	
MAY 7 '65	NOV 10 1988	
MAY 8 '65		
MAY 27 '65	DEC 13 1989	
DEC 4 '65	NOV 24 1991	
JAN - 3 1966	NOV 17 1992	
FEB 22 1966	DEC 01 1992	
MAR 1 1966	FEB 27 1993	
MAY 4 1966	OCT 02 1993	
APR 29 1969	MAR 19 1997	
MAY 12 1969	DEC 04 2001	
FEB 4 1970		
4 1971		

PRINTED IN U.S.A.